漫画中国思想系列

Chinese Thought Comic Series

智者的低语

老子说

THE DAO SPEAKS

Whispers of Wisdom

蔡志忠 / 编绘

[美] 布莱恩·布雅 / 译

中国出版集团

现代出版社

图字：01-2005-0834

图书在版编目（CIP）数据

老子说 / 蔡志忠编绘；（美）布雅（Bruya,B.）译.
-- 北京：现代出版社,2013.8
（蔡志忠漫画中国传统文化经典：中英文对照版）
ISBN 978-7-5143-1665-0

Ⅰ．①老… Ⅱ．①蔡… ②布… Ⅲ．①漫画—连环画
—作品集—中国—现代 Ⅳ．① J228.2

中国版本图书馆CIP数据核字（2013）第181218号

蔡志忠漫画中国传统文化经典：中英文对照版

老子说

作　　者	蔡志忠　编绘
	［美］布莱恩·布雅（BRIAN BRUYA）译
责任编辑	崔晓燕
出版发行	现代出版社
地　　址	北京市安定门外安华里 504 号
邮政编码	100011
电　　话	010-64267325　010-64245264（兼传真）
网　　址	www.1980xd.com
电子信箱	xiandai@cnpitc.com.cn
印　　刷	三河市南阳印刷有限公司
开　　本	710×1000　1/16
印　　张	12.5
版　　次	2013 年 9 月第 1 版　2016 年 12 月第 6 次印刷
书　　号	ISBN 978-7-5143-1665-0
定　　价	23.00 元

目录
contents

老子说　智者的低语
The Dao Speaks Whispers of Wisdom 1

生命的大智慧　*The Wisdom of Life* 3

老子其犹龙乎　*Is Not Laozi Like the Dragon!* 7

第一部分　Part I :
道（上篇） *The Way* 13

道可道，非常道　*The Dao That Can't Be Spoken* 14

有无相生　*The Theory of Relativity* 18

无为　*Favors* 20

道冲　*The Dao Is Empty* 22

刍狗　*Straw Dogs* 23

天地　*Our World Eternal* 25

上善若水　*Virtue Resembles Water* 26

持而盈之　*The Overflowing Cup* 28

营魄抱一　*Body and Soul* 30

无　*The Empty Cup* 31

无欲　*Boundless Desires* 33

宠辱　*Honor's Disgrace* 35

守静　*Maintaining Tranquillity* 37

太上　*The Invisible King* 39

仁义　*Regression into Benevolence* 41

绝学　*Living With the Dao* 43

曲则全　*Bend Don't Break* 45

胜而不美　*Victory Is Not Proud* 47

自知　*Overcoming Yourself* 49

执"大道"　*Holding on to the Dao* 51

以柔克刚　*The Strength of Weakness* 52

第二部分　Part Ⅱ :
道（下篇）*The Way* 53
玄牝　*The Mysterious Female* 54
无物　*The Dao is Indistinct* 55
古之得"道"者　*Daoists of Old* 57
绝圣弃智　*The Artificial Role Model* 60
道之为物　*Reality of the Dao* 61
希言自然　*The Wanton Ruler* 63
企者不立　*The Exhibitionist* 66
有物浑成　*The Beginning* 68
处重守静　*The Serious Ruler* 70
善行无辙迹　*Sagely Conservation* 72
为天下豁　*Confluence of the World* 75
欲取天下　*A Natural Government* 78
不矜不伐　*War and Force* 80
本诸自然　*A Natural Balance* 82
大道氾兮　*The Dao Nurtures* 84
道常无为　*The Natural Ruler* 85

第三部分　Part Ⅲ :
德（上篇）*The Virtue* 86
上德无为　*Superior Virtue Is Not Virtue* 87
有生于无　*Getting Something From Nothing* 89
道生万物　*Universal Harmony* 90
至柔　*Soft Will Overcome* 91
知足不辱　*The Risk of Seeking Fame and Fortune* 92
欲得　*There Is No Greater Crime* 93
不行而知　*Don't Go Out* 95
无为　*In Pursuit of Non-action* 96
圣人　*The Ideal Leader* 97
咒虎　*A Tiger May Be Vicious* 98

玄同　*One Who Speaks Does Not Know*.. 101

无欲自朴　*The More Laws There Are*... 102

烹小鲜　*Frying Fish*.. 104

乐推　*Navigating the State*... 105

不争　*The Good General*... 106

知知　*The Know-it-all*.. 107

不争善胜　*Contend By Not Contending*... 108

草木　*Tree vs. Grass*.. 110

水石　*Water vs. Rock*.. 112

予而不取　*It's Better to Give Than to Receive*... 113

圣人不积　*The More You Give, the More You Get*..114

第四部分　Part IV：

德（下篇） *The Virtue*.. 116

得一者　*Obtaining the One*.. 117

士闻道　*The Level Path*... 121

大成若缺　*A Model for the World*... 125

道生之，德畜之　*Profound Virtue*... 127

天下有始　*The Doors of Perception*... 129

大道　*The Great Path*.. 131

善建者不拔　*Cultivating Virtue*... 133

含德之厚　*An Infant's Virtue*.. 135

奇正无端　*There Is No Justice*... 138

俭啬　*Frugality*.. 140

大者宜为下　*The Lowly Superpower*... 142

道者万物之奥　*Prizing the Dao*... 144

多易必多难　*Easing Difficulties*.. 146

慎终如始　*Planning and Perseverance*... 148

以愚治国　*Mysterious Virtue*.. 150

三宝　*The Three Treasures*.. 152

用兵　*Warfare*.. 154

圣人怀玉　*Heart of Jade*... 156

民不畏威　*Tyranny*.. 158

代大匠斲　*Standing In for the Carpenter* 160

民之饥　*Starvation and Taxes* 162

天道犹张弓　*The Drawn Bow* 163

小国寡民　*The Ideal Country* 165

第五部分　Part V :
诸子谈黄老经　*Ancient Thinkers Discuss the Dao* 168

道可道，非常道。　*If the Dao can be explained, it is not the constant Dao.* 169

名可名，非常名。　*If a name can be named, it is not a constant name.* 171

太上，不知有之。　*As for the greatest kind of ruler,*

　　you don't even know he's there. 172

人法地，地法天，天法道，道法自然。　*People follow the earth, the earth*

　　follows heaven, heaven follows the Dao, the Dao follows nature. 173

上德不德，是以有德；下德不失德，是以无德。　*People of superior virtue*

　　are not so intentionally and are therefore virtuous. People of inferior virtue are

　　intentionally virtuous and are thus not virtuous. 174

祸莫大于不知足，咎莫大于欲得。　*There is no greater disaster than*

　　discontentment. There is no greater crime than greed. 175

知者不言，言者不知。

　　One who knows does not speak, One who speaks does not know. 176

天下多忌讳，而民弥贫；朝多利器，国家滋昏；人多伎巧，奇物滋起。

　　The more prohibitions there are, the poorer the people will be.

　　The more weapons there are, the more discordant it will be.

　　The more cunning people are, the more wickedness there will be. 177

善为士者，不武；善战者，不怒；善胜敌者，不与。

　　A good general is not excessively violent, A good soldier is not easily angered,

　　A good conqueror does not resort to confrontation. 178

附录·延伸阅读　*APPENDIX Further reading* 179

老子说　智者的低语
The Dao Speaks
Whispers of Wisdom

老子 Laozi

根据中国最伟大的史学家司马迁记载：

老子姓李名耳，字聃。

是楚国苦县厉乡曲仁里人，周藏书室的管理人员。

老子修道德，他的学说以自隐无名为主。久住周国，看到周国衰微下去，于是离去。向西经过函谷关时，关令尹喜说："你将去隐居，请尽力为我著书吧！"于是老子写下《道德经》两卷五千余字，渺然出关，不知终老于何处。

According to China's greatest historian Sima Qian:

Laozi's surname was Li, his given name was Er, and his coming-of-age name was Dan.

He was a native of the village of Quren, Li district, Hu county, in the state of Chu, and he worked as caretaker of the imperial archives in Zhou.

Laozi (Lao-tzu) spoke of the Way and the Virtue, focusing on self-effacement and not seeking a name for oneself. He resided for a long while in Zhou, and, witnessing the decline of the Zhou empire, he decided to leave. He went west, and when he was about to head out through Hangu pass, Yin Xi the gatekeeper said to him:"Since you are going off to live in reclusion, perhaps you could write down a few of your ideas for me first." So Laozi proceeded to write the Dao De Jing in two books totaling just over 5,000 words. He then departed, and no one knows what became of him.

生命的大智慧
The Wisdom of Life

自古以来，一般的教诲都是：
From the most ancient times, the standard teachings had been:

人要表现坚强，不可柔弱，人要表现聪明，不要愚鲁！
You must exhibit your strength and intelligence; don't let people think you are weak or foolish.

1

不过，中国历史上却出现一位"老子"与众不同。
However, a very unique man named Laozi appeared early on in Chinese history.

2

3

人要表现柔弱，不要刚强！人要表现愚鲁，不要聪明！人要无为、无我、无欲、居下、清虚、自然……
Exhibit weakness and foolishness; don't let people think you are strong or intelligent. Remember the importance of non-action, no-self, no-desires, humility, tranquillity, being natural...

一般人都认为刚强好啊！
Most people think that being strong is good!

刚强的容易折断，柔弱的才能够保全。
But strength will break where weakness will remain intact.

4

比如说，你身上什么最硬？什么最软？
For instance, what's the hardest part of your body? And what's the softest?

牙齿最硬！舌头最软！
My teeth are the hardest, and my tongue is the softest.

5

你看，到了我这年纪，牙齿全部脱落了，舌头却完好无恙。
Take a look, I'm so old that my teeth have all fallen out, yet my tongue is just fine.

6

大树比小草刚强吧？
A huge tree is stronger than a tiny blade of grass, right?

是啊！
Right!

7

台风来的时候，大树经常被连根拔起，小草却完好无恙。
But in a typhoon, it's the huge tree that gets pulled up by the force of the wind, while the tiny grass just sways back and forth.

8

风无形无体，却能够倒屋拔树。
Although the wind has no form or body, it can blow down houses and uproot trees.

9

水可方可圆，能够怀山襄陵。这不是说明了刚强的未必是强，柔弱才是真正的强吗？
Water is the most pliable of things, and yet it can erode away mountains and carve out canyons. This should explain that firmness isn't necessarily strength, while weakness actually is strength.

10

11
一般人认为聪明好，但一个智者应该表现愚鲁，大智若愚。
Most people think that intelligence is good, but a wise person should exhibit foolishness. Great wisdom appears to be foolishness.

12
大富翁通常深藏不露。
Wealthy people often give the appearance of having nothing.

哈哈哈，我没有多少财产啦！
No, no. I don't have much money at all.

13
反之，一个双手戴满金戒、嘴装金牙、颈挂金链的人，家里可能是空空如也。
On the other hand, a person with diamond rings, gold fillings, and gold chains around his neck may be returning to an empty house.

哼！只是外表装阔的家伙。
Hmph! Show off.

14
如果想有所成就，一定要把全部的智力、精力集中在一点，而在其他方面做一个愚者才行。
If you want to be a success, concentrate all of your energy and intelligence on one thing and play the fool in all others.

15
请问你诗、书、画样样都行吗？
Excuse me, are you good at writing, painting, and all that other stuff?

对不起！我只懂得下棋，其他方面不行！
Sorry, I only know chess.

16
哈哈哈，我诗、书、画都有研究！
Ha, ha. I've studied them all—writing, painting, everything!

17
你最精的是什么？
And what are you best at?

什……什么都不精……
Well... I... um... I guess...none, really...

他是围棋第一高手呢！
He's the grand master of chess!

我只是皮毛之见，什么都只懂点点……
I guess I'm just a jack of all trades and master of none...

人不能处处装聪明，想面面俱到，路路皆通，结果变成肤浅之知，路路不通。
If you try to learn everything about everything, you'll just end up with a superficial knowledge leading nowhere.

18

19

一般人只能看到事物的表面，而老子却能看到里面。
Most people can only see the surface of things, but Laozi could see what was on the inside, as well.

21

老子认为柔弱就能谦下不争；愚鲁就能弃华取实。一切依循自然。
Laozi believed that weakness allows us to be humble and noncontentious, and that through foolishness, we can do away with the superficial and get down to reality. Everything in accordance with nature.

一般人只能看到事物的正面，而老子却能看到反面。
Most people can only see the face of things, but Laozi could see the back, as well.

利的。
Sharp.

可是这一面却是钝的。
Yes, but this side is blunt.

20

22

老子的思想恢廓有容，可大可久，能处顺境，也能处逆境，虽遇挫折打击，也能承受不倒，还能迂曲转进。
Laozi's thinking was vast and all-inclusive, everlasting and adaptable, able to adjust in adversity and if obstructed or attacked, able to wind around and continue forward.

23

老子反对物欲，讲求精神生活，反对人为，讲求体法自然；重视精神生活，以精神来役使物质。
Laozi was opposed to material desires, favoring instead a spiritual life. He was opposed to unnecessary action, preferring to follow nature. He emphasized the spirit, making material things subservient to it.

24

6

老子其犹龙乎
Is Not
Laozi
Like the Dragon!

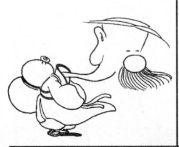

二千五百多年前世界上几个古老的文明国家都呈现了极为灿烂的文化，一些杰出的学者和思想家纷纷产生。在希腊，有大哲学家泰勒斯和赫拉克利特。

About twenty-five centuries ago, sophisticated cultures flourished in several parts of the world. These cultures brought forth outstanding scholars and thinkers. In Greece, there were the great philosophers Thales and Heraclitus.

1

2

在印度，则有佛教的创始人释迦牟尼。

In India, Siddhā rtha Gautama founded the Buddhist religion.

4

其中以儒、道、墨、法四家影响最大，而道家学派的创始人便是老子。

Of these, the most influential were the Confucianists, Daoists, Moists, and Legalists. A great communicator of what came to be known as the Daoist school was a man we call Laozi.

3

在中国，春秋战国时期（公元前 770—221 年），百家争鸣，流派纷纭。

In China, during the Spring & Autumn and Warring States periods (770~221 BC), numerous schools of thought arose and competed vigorously for domination.

杂
Misce-laneous

墨
Moism

纵横
Diplo-tists

名
Names

道
Daoism

阴阳
Yin Yang

法
Legalism

儒
Confu-cianism

农
Agricul-turists

老子姓李，名耳，字聃。于西周末年诞生于楚国苦县历乡曲仁里。

According to certain historical records, Laozi's surname was Li, given name Er, and coming-of-age name Dan. He was born in the sixth century B.C. in Quren village, Li district, Hu county, in the state of Chu.

1

周朝曾召他做守藏室的史官。

Legend has it that he was appointed caretaker of the state archives under King Wu of Zhou.

2

借这两本书。
I'd like to borrow two books, please.

请在这里登记。
O.k., sign right here.

3

在这里，他更潜心于书籍之中，所习得鉴往知来的历史，使他对人也有更深切的体认。

Here, Laozi pored through innumerable books, absorbing the knowledge of the times and gaining many insights into life.

4

就这样，老子的智慧一日一日增长着。
And in this way, Laozi grew wiser by the day.

5

6

大教育家孔子来访!
The great educator Confucius is coming to visit.

你们先把路打扫干净，我去迎接他。
Ok., you fellows go clean up the road, and I'll go out to meet him.

7

于是老子便骑着牛，到郊外去迎接。
Laozi mounted up and went to the outskirts of town to meet Confucius.

8

9

孔子也依照当时的礼节，从自己的车上下来，捧着作为见面礼的大雁，送给老子。
According to the etiquette of the time, Confucius descended from his carriage and presented Laozi with a wild goose.

孔子在洛阳住了几天，并向老子请教了很多事情。
Confucius stayed with Laozi in Luoyang for several days, learning many things.

谢谢先生教诲，受益良多。告辞了。
Thank you, sir, for imparting your wisdom. I must take leave now.

我送你两句话当临别的礼物吧。
Let me mention two more things before you go.

一、你所钻研的多半是古人的东西，可是古人死了，连骨头也烂了，不过剩下那么几句话。你不能把那些话看得太死。
One, most of what you are studying and teaching are the thoughts of the ancients, but these ancients are dead— even their bones are rotten, and yet a few of their words remain. Don't place too much emphasis on what they said.

二、有极高道德的人都是很朴实的。你应该去掉骄傲、贪恋，去掉一些架子、妄想，这对你是有好处的。
Two, those of superlative virtue are all very simple people. Eliminate your pride and desires and get rid of your airs and ambitions, for they will be of no benefit to you.

10

孔子怀着感激的心情离开了洛阳，回到鲁国后，常常赞美老子。
Confucius left Luoyang full of gratitude and after returning to his native state of Lu, often praised Laozi's wisdom.

鸟，我知道它会飞。
I know birds can fly.

鱼，我知道它会游水。
I know fish can swim.

兽，我知道它会走。
I know beasts can walk.

13　14　15

但是龙，它在云端，在天上，无法捉摸，深不可测。李聃就像龙一样啊！
But dragons, they are in the clouds, in the heavens, ungraspable, unfathomable. Is not Laozi like the dragon!

16

11

老子看到周室逐渐衰微，便离开洛阳，西出函谷关。
In the twenty-third year of the Zhou king Zhao, witnessing the gradual decline of the House of Zhou, Laozi departed Luoyang and journeyed westward through the Hangu pass of the Great Wall.

17

18

我是守官令尹喜，也非常喜欢道术。
I'm the gate keeper, In Xi, and I am very interested in the Daoist art.

19

先生就将隐居，是否可为我写些东西，好教我有所依循来处事？
Do you think before you leave, you could jot down a few notes on Daoism for me?

于是老子就写了一本书，分为上、下篇，共有五千多字。
So Laozi wrote a short book in two parts, consisting of just over five thousand words.

20

道
the Way

德
the Virtue

老子写好以后，就出关走了，从此就没有人知道他的下落。
Upon finishing the book, he passed through the Great Wall and was never heard from again.

21

第一部分：
Part I :

道

（上篇）

The Way

道可道，非常道
The Dao That Can't Be Spoken

1

"道"是如此这般的……
The Dao is like this, it does this, and it isn't this...

啊，我懂了！
Oh, I get it!

2

错了，"道"如果可以说得明白，解释得清楚，就不是"道"了。
Excuse me, but I believe you are mistaken. If you can explain the Dao clearly, then that is not the Dao.

3

"道"包含万物之理。没有形状，没有声音，没有实体，并且永恒不变。这道理不是用语言、文字所能解说得明白的。
The Dao encompasses the principles of the myriad things. It is formless, silent, has no body, and is eternal and unchanging. This principle cannot be clearly explained through language.

9

当"道"一产生创生的作用，万物就随之
而生，可称之为"有"。
这"有"就是"道"的作用。
*When the Dao produced the function of
creation, the myriad things came forth.
This we call "Being". This Being is the
function of the Dao.*

所以，当想到天地的本始是"无"，就可以了
解道的本体精微奥妙。
*So, when we understand that in the beginning
there was Nothing, we can come to comprehend the subtlety and mystery of the Dao's
substance.*

想到万物的根源是"有"，就可以了解道的作用广大无边。
*When we understand that the origin of the myriad things is
Being, we can come to comprehend the vastness and limitles-
sness of the Dao's function.*

10

11

"无"和"有"，一是道的本体，一是道的作用，可以说同出于道，只是名称不同而已！
12

Nothing and Being — one is the substance, and the other is the function. You can say they both come from the Dao, they just have different names is all!

都可以称为玄妙，玄妙而又玄妙啊！
13

They can both be called mysterious, even more mysterious than mysterious!

那就是宇宙万物创生的本原"道"了。
14

Yes, that's the Dao, the source of creation for the universe and the myriad things.

宇宙的本体是"无"。由"无"而生天地，由天地而生万物，终于形成了万象纷纭的世界。

The underlying substance of the universe is Nothingness. From Nothing came heaven and earth. From heaven and earth came the myriad things, finally giving rise to the world as we know it.

有无相生
The Theory of Relativity

1

天下都知道美之所以为美。
When people realize what beauty is.

美
Beautiful

2

丑的观念也产生了。
The concept of ugliness arises as well.

丑
Ugly

3

天下都知道善之所以为善。
When people realize what goodness is.

善
Good

4

不善
bad

不善的观念也产生了。
The concept of badness arises also.

5

有和无是互相比较而生的。
Being and Nothing produce each other.

无
Nothing

有
Being

6

难和易是互相比较而成的。
Easy and difficult create each other.

易
Easy

难
Difficult

7

长和短是互相比较而显现的。
Long and short reveal each other.

长
Long

短
Short

8

高
High

高和下是互相比较而造成倾倚的。
High and low support each other.

下
Low

9

音和声是互相对应而产生和谐的。
Sound and voice harmonize with each other.

10

后
Back

前
Front

前和后是互相对应而形成顺序的。
Front and back follow each other.

11

所以"圣人"以无为的态度来处理世事，实行"不言"的教导。
So the sage acts without doing and teaches without speaking.

任万物兴作而不加主宰；
生长万物而不据为己有；
作育万物而不自恃己能；
功业成就而不自居。
He causes the movement of the myriad things but does not control them; He creates the myriad things but does not take them as his own; He nurtures the myriad things but does not presume upon his abilities; He succeeds in his endeavors but does not dwell on his success.

正因他不居功，所以功绩不会埋没。
And it is because he doesn't dwell on his successes that they are not obscured.

人间世上一切的概念、价值都是人所设定的，价值判断都是因比较而产生的。而对应的关系是经常变动着的，因此价值判断也在不断地变动中。美和丑、有和无、难和易、长和短、高和下、前和后等都要淡然处之，不要庸人自扰才好。
All ideas and values are established by people, and value judgments come through comparisons. But the way we look at things must constantly change, and thus our value judgments must constantly change. So when dealing with beautiful and ugly, being and nothing, difficult and easy, long and short, high and low, front and back, etc., take them lightly and don't get excited over nothing.

12

13

无 为
Favors

8

不珍贵难得的货品，可以使人民不起盗心。
By not placing value on things difficult to obtain, you can keep people from wanting to steal things.

9

名
Fame

不显现名利的可贪，可以使人民的心思不被惑乱。
By not rewarding fame, you can keep people from muddling their minds with it.

所以圣人为政，要净化人民的心思，满足人民的安饱，减损人民的心志，增强人民的体魄。
So a sage governs by purifying the hearts of the people. He keeps people secure and satisfied, eliminates their scheming ambitions, and strengthens their bodies.

10

常使人民没有伪诈的心智，没有争盗的欲念，使一些自作聪明的人不敢妄为。
He causes the people to have no deceptive knowledge or covetous desires. He causes the cunning ones to refrain from engaging in unsavory acts.

11

12

这样顺其自然、无私无我的治理，国家就没有什么治理不好的了。
By acting in accordance with nature and governing selflessly, there will be nothing in the country that is not well-governed.

"名位"引起人的争逐，"财货"激起人的贪图。于是巧诈伪作就层出不穷了，这是导致社会混乱冲突的主要原因啊！
Fame and position incite contention, wealth excites people's greed. As a result, lying and deceit arise in endless succession, and these lead to confusion and conflicts in society!

道 冲
The Dao
Is Empty

1

"道"体是空虚的，然而作用却不穷竭。
The substance of the Dao is empty, but its function is inexhaustible.

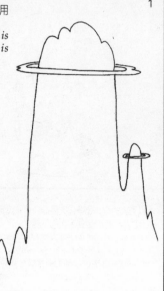

2

这样的渊深，却能创生万物，是万物的本原。它虽然隐没无形，似亡而又实存。
This vastness produced the myriad things, is the original source of the myriad things. It is invisible and without form, seemingly non-existent, yet it is present.

3

我不知道它是从哪里产生的，似乎有天帝以前就有了它。
I don't know where it comes from, but it seems to have existed even before the god of heaven.

"道"体是虚状的，这虚体并不是一无所有，它含藏着无尽的创造因子。因而它的作用是不穷竭的。这个虚状的"道"体，是万物的根源。
This emptiness of the Dao doesn't mean a complete vacuity, for it conceals innumerable seeds of creation. And that is why its function is inexhaustible. This empty substance called the "Dao" is the origin of the myriad things.

刍狗
Straw Dogs

天地是大公无私的，对万物一视同仁，把万物当做草扎的狗一样，没有喜爱，没有憎恨。
Nature holds no prejudice and cares for all things the same. It views everything as so many straw dogs, neither loving nor hating them.

圣人也是大公无私的，把百姓当做草扎的狗一样，没有喜爱、没有憎恨，全部一视同仁。
The sage also holds no prejudice, seeing the people as so many straw dogs, neither loving nor hating them, but looking after them all equally.

3

天地之间，就好像风箱一样，中间是空虚的。但正因其空虚，所以才能够化生万物。
The space between heaven and earth is like a bellows. Although it is empty, it is because of its emptiness that it is able to produce the myriad things.

由此可见，多所作为，多所设施，反而招致错误、失败。
From this we see that doing too much and taking on too much can lead to mistakes and failure.

4

大道创生万物，纯任自然，无偏无私。国君治政，也应该效法这种精神，无为不言，与民相安，社会自然安宁。
The Dao produces the myriad things, lets nature take its course, and is selfless and unprejudiced. Rulers should take this as their model, governing through non-action and silence and living at peace with the people, which in the end, leads to a naturally tranquil society.

5

还不如抱守清虚、无为不言来得好。
It is better to preserve tranquillity, non-action, and silence.

天 地
Our World
Eternal

1

天地所以能够长久，乃是因为它的一切运作都不为自己，所以能够长久。

Heaven and earth are everlasting because they do not exist for themselves.

2

圣人处处谨虚、退让，反而能够赢得爱戴。

In all he does, a sage is modest and yields to others, and as a result, wins the adoration of others.

3

事事不计较利害得失，反而身受其益。

He gives no thought to profit and loss, and yet is benefited by this.

4

这不正是由于他不自私，结果反而成全了自己！

Because he is unselfish, he ends up achieving what is in his own best interest!

谦让反而能赢得爱戴，处处为别人着想，反而能够成就自己的理想。

Modesty wins adoration. By doing things for others, you can accomplish your own ideals.

上善若水
Virtue Resembles
Water

有道德的人就像水一样！
A virtuous person is like water!

1

水有三种特性，第一是能够滋养万物。
Water has three special characteristics: One, it nurtures the myriad things.

2

第二是本性柔弱，顺自然而不争。
Two, it is naturally pliant-flowing where nature takes it.

3

第三是蓄居流注于人人所厌恶的卑下之处。
Three, it resides in lowly places despised by people.

4

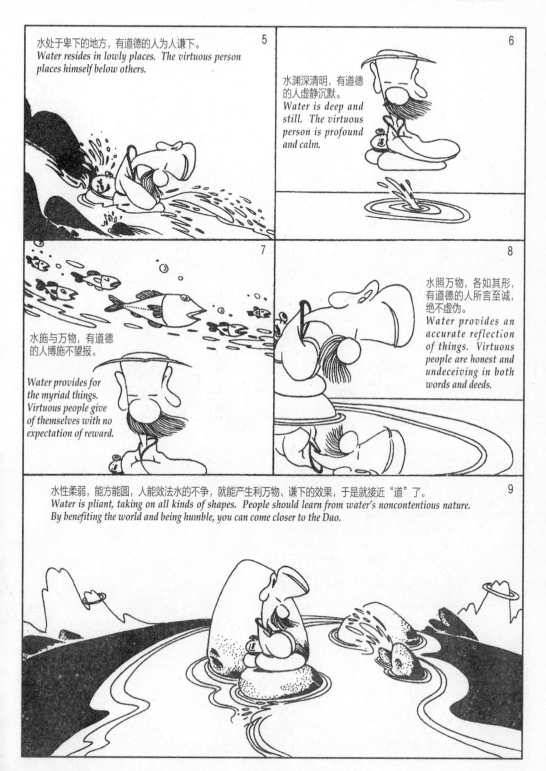

5
水处于卑下的地方，有道德的人为人谦下。
Water resides in lowly places. The virtuous person places himself below others.

6
水渊深清明，有道德的人虚静沉默。
Water is deep and still. The virtuous person is profound and calm.

7
水施与万物，有道德的人博施不望报。
Water provides for the myriad things. Virtuous people give of themselves with no expectation of reward.

8
水照万物，各如其形，有道德的人所言至诚，绝不虚伪。
Water provides an accurate reflection of things. Virtuous people are honest and undeceiving in both words and deeds.

9
水性柔弱，能方能圆，人能效法水的不争，就能产生利万物、谦下的效果，于是就接近"道"了。
Water is pliant, taking on all kinds of shapes. People should learn from water's noncontentious nature. By benefiting the world and being humble, you can come closer to the Dao.

持而盈之
The Overflowing Cup

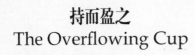

盛在任何器皿里的水，太满了就要溢出来。
Regardless of the vessel, if more water is poured in than it can hold, it will overflow.

1

2

够了，够了，八分满就够了！
That's enough, that's enough, just below the rim is fine!

3

刀锥能用就行了，如果磨得太锐利……
A knife is as long as it is sharp, but one that is sharpened too much...

4

锋芒太露，就很容易折断。
Is easily broken.

一个人金银财宝太多了，会遭到别人的觊觎。
If a person has too much wealth, it will arouse the envy of others.

5

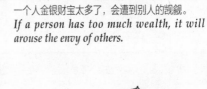

也会因生活糜烂，最后反而不能保有这些财宝。
And through an overly luxurious life, that wealth will eventually be lost.

6

完了……钱花光了……
Oh no... it's gone! I'm broke...

7

所以人在成功之后，就激流勇退，这才合于自然之道。
After achieving success, one should step gracefully aside. This is in keeping with the natural Dao.

8

就像上天一样：
上天生万物，也是生而不有，为而不恃，功成而不居啊……
It is like heaven, which created all things but possesses nothing, nurtures but does not presume, succeeds but does not dwell on the success...

9

29

营魄抱一
Body and Soul

1

心中紧守着道，精神和形体合一，能不分离吗？

In embracing the Dao and allowing your spirit and body to become one, can you keep them from being separated?

2

听任生理的本能，导致最柔和的心境，能像婴儿一样吗？

In letting your basic instincts lead you to a most tender frame of mind, can you come to resemble an infant?

3

摒除心智的作用，能没有瑕疵吗？

In cleansing your mind, can you be without blemishes?

4

爱国治民，能自然无为吗？

In loving your country and governing the people well, can you reach a natural state of non-action?

无为
Non-action

5

感官和外界接触，能安静谨慎吗？

In coming into sensual contact with the outside world, can you be calm and cautious?

道
Dao

6

智无不照，能不用心机吗？

In comprehending all the things around you, can you do so without ulterior motives?

生活必须是形体和精神合一而不偏离。能守"道"，可使肉体生活与精神生活臻至一种和谐的状况。

Life is a melding of the body and soul. If you can preserve the Dao, you can achieve harmony of body and soul.

无
The Empty Cup

世人只知道"有"的利益，而不知道"无"的用处。
People only seem to understand the benefits of Being, not realizing the advantages of Nothing.

事实上，"无"的用处比"有"要大得多。
Nothing can actually have more uses than Being.

1

三十根车辐汇集在车毂，因为车毂是空虚的，车才能产生乘坐的作用。
Thirty spokes come together in the center of a wheel, but it is the emptiness of the hub that gives the wheel its usefulness.

无
Nothing

2

一个杯子，
A cup,

3

因为中间的空虚，才能产生盛物的作用。
It is because the cup is empty in the middle, that it can be filled and is thus useful.

无
Nothing

有
Being

4

31

无欲
Boundless Desires

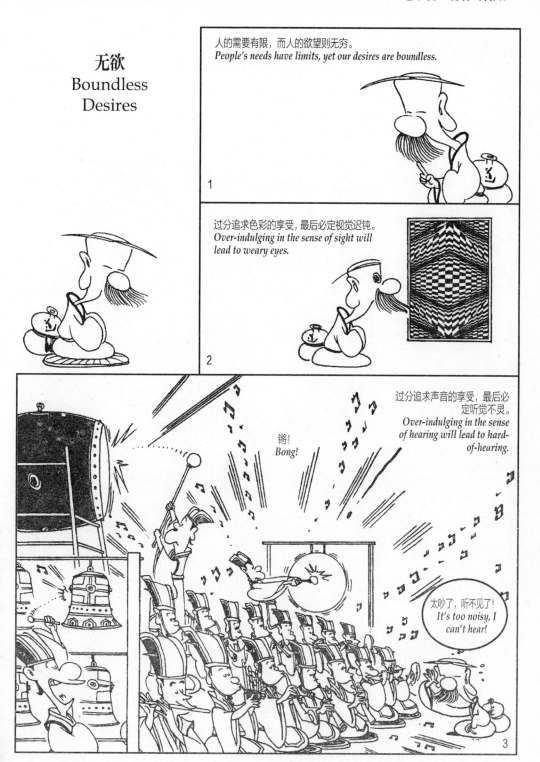

1

人的需要有限，而人的欲望则无穷。
People's needs have limits, yet our desires are boundless.

2

过分追求色彩的享受，最后必定视觉迟钝。
Over-indulging in the sense of sight will lead to weary eyes.

过分追求声音的享受，最后必定听觉不灵。
Over-indulging in the sense of hearing will lead to hard-of-hearing.

锵!
Bong!

太吵了，听不见了!
It's too noisy, I can't hear!

3

过分追求味道的享受，最后必定味觉丧失，食不知味。
Over-indulging in the sense of taste will lead to a loss of appetite.

过分纵情于玩乐，最后必定弄得心神不宁，神不守舍。
Over-indulging in entertainment will lead to nervous agitation.

4

5

过分追求金银珠宝，最后必行伤德坏，身败名裂。
Over-zealously pursuing wealth will lead to injury of your moral character and reputation.

6

7

欲海难填，不能去欲，必遭灭顶。过分追求欲望而不能节制，其结果不仅不能感到满足、舒适，反而会感到痛苦，丧失自我。
"The sea of desires is difficult to stay" — if you cannot rid yourself of desires, you will surely drown. A person with uncontrollable desires will not only be unable to feel satisfied or comfortable, but conversely, will feel pain and will harm his sense of self.

无欲
No
Desires

所以体道的圣人，生活简单，只求填饱肚子，不求官能享受。宁取质朴宁静，不求奢侈浮华。
Therefore, the sage who understands the Dao, lives a simple life, eating only until full and not pursuing sensual pleasures. He is satisfied with a quiet life and not concerned with luxury and splendor.

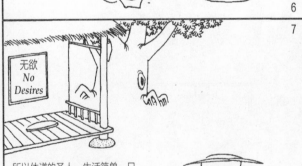

宠 辱
Honor's
Disgrace

世人得失名利的心太重，所以得到荣宠和受到屈辱都身惊害怕。

Because people are too concerned with fame and fortune, whether they are honored or disgraced, they are always apprehensive.

宠
Honor

辱
Disgrace

1

畏惧大的祸患，也因而身惊。为什么呢？

They constantly fear disaster and harm themselves by this. What is the reason?

2

因为在世人的心目中，荣宠是高尚的，得到荣宠就觉得高贵，因而怕失去荣宠。

It is because people believe that honor is something to be prized, that winning the respect of others is the noblest of things. It is on account of this, that they are terrified of losing their honor.

3

守 静
Maintaining Tranquillity

人的心灵本来是虚明、宁静。
People's souls are originally vacuous and tranquil.

1

2

玉
Jade!

但往往为私欲所蒙蔽。
But somehow we are always blinded by selfish desire.

因而观物不得其正，行事则失其常。
As a result, we cannot view things clearly, and our actions lose their constancy.

3

4

所以我们要尽力使心回复到虚明宁静的状态。这样就能够看清万物蓬勃生长，看出往复循环的道理。
Thus, we must try to return to a state of vacuity and tranquillity. This way, we can witness the flourishing of the myriad things, we can see the recurrent cycles of the natural process.

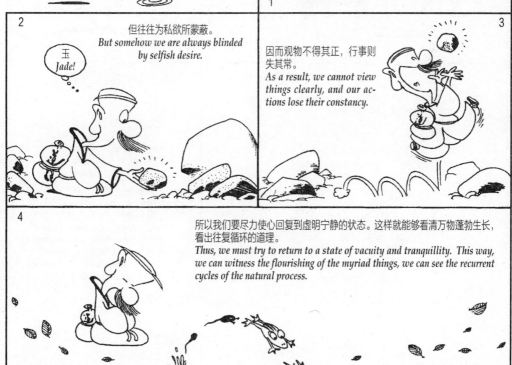

万物纷纷纭纭，各自返回到它的根本，这叫做"静"，也叫做"常"。了解"常"叫做"明"。不了解"常"而轻举妄动，就会有祸害。

The myriad things are many and varied, and eventually each one returns to its source. This is called "tranquillity". It is also called "constancy". Understanding constancy is called "enlightenment". Those who do not understand constancy and are rash and impulsive will eventually encounter great trouble.

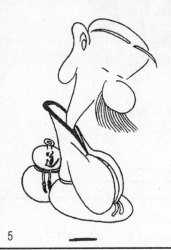

5

了解"常道"的人是无所不包的；就能坦然大公，才能做到无不周遍，才能符合自然，才能符合于"道"。

One who understands the "constant Dao" is all-encompassing; being all-encompassing, one is open and just; being open and just, one is universal; being universal, one is in accord with nature; being in accord with nature, one is in accord with the Dao.

6

符合"大道"才能永垂不朽，这样，终身也不会有任何危险了。
By being in accord with the Dao, we gain longevity, and longevity means a life free from danger.

7

"致虚"和"守静"的功夫做到极笃，就能明察事理，能洞知万物变化的常规，就能深得自然的妙趣，而与"道"同体。

Through "attaining vacuity" and "maintaining tranquillity", you will come to clearly examine the principles of the world and thoroughly understand the transformations of the myriad things. You will be able to profoundly appreciate nature's subtleties and become one with the Dao.

太 上
The
Invisible King

国君治理国政，可分为四个等级。最上等的国君，推行不言的教化，使人民各顺其性、各安其生。
There are four different levels of rulers. The highest is the one who leads without words, allowing the people to follow their own natures and live in their own way.

我只知道有国君，但不知道他到底为我们做些什么？
King?
Do we have a king?

次一等的国君，用德教感化人民，用仁义治理人民。
The next highest is the ruler who uses goodness to transform the people and benevolence and righteousness to govern them.

我们的国君很棒，为我们做了很多事情！
We have a wonderful king. He's done many things for us!

3

第三等的国君，用政教治理人民，用刑法威吓人民。
The next is the ruler who controls his people with political teachings and scares his people into submission through stringent laws and severe punishments.

我们的国君管我们很严、很凶，很可怕！
Our king is very strict, very harsh, very terrifying!

4

第四等的国君，用权术愚弄人民，用诡计欺骗人民。
The worst kind of ruler uses all of his powers to toy with the people and cheats them through devious schemes.

我们的国君太欺负老百姓了，我们要起来抗暴！
We're being oppressed! It's time to revolt!

5

最好的政治是"无为而治"，人民各顺其性，各安其生，得到了最大的益处。功成事遂，老百姓还浑然不觉，说是自然如此的哩！
The best way to govern is through "non-action"– allowing the people to follow their natures and live in their own way. When everything is accomplished without the people even knowing anything was attempted, that is when we can say that it was naturally so!

这是我们自然如此的啊！
We are naturally this way!

为政者，像是肺之于人体，最好的肺是你没感到有它在替我们呼吸工作。当你天天感到肺在替你呼吸，那么，这个肺已经有病了！
A government can be compared to our lungs. Our lungs are best when we don't realize they are helping us breathe. It is when we are constantly aware of our lungs that we know they have come down with an illness.

仁义
Regression into Benevolence

1

上古的时候，人民诚实，不识不知，根本没有虚伪。

In the early days of civilization, people were simple and honest. They couldn't read, and they didn't know much, but at the same time, they weren't greedy or dishonest.

用智慧来防止逃税！

I'll have to use my head to keep him from evading taxes.

中古的时候，民情日凿，于是治天下的人就用他的智慧创造了制度法令来治理人民。

Later on in history, people became more and more cunning. As a result, government leaders were forced to use their intelligence to create a legal system to keep the people in line.

用智慧来逃税！

I'll have to use my head to avoid paying taxes.

于是虚伪诡诈也随之而产生了。

This is when hypocrisy and deceit arose.

2

3

家族中人都能坦诚相与、和睦相处，根本就用不着孝和慈。

Originally, families were happy and the members got along very well with each other. There was no need for such concepts as "filial piety" or "parental kindness".

等到六亲失和，孝和慈才因而产生了。

But when family relationships began to breakdown, concepts such as these became important.

要和睦！要孝顺！要听话！

Be nice! Respect your elders! Be good!

4

41

国家清明的时候，臣子们各司其所，各尽其职，没有所谓的忠臣。
When the country was still pure and innocent, government ministers all did what they were supposed to, and there was no such thing as a "loyal minister".

他们都是我的臣子！
They are all my ministers!

5

国家昏乱以后，臣子不能负责尽职，忠臣才随之产生了。
But when the country fell into chaos, and ministers began scheming among themselves, the words "loyal minister" became necessary.

仁义、智慧、孝慈、忠臣，这些都是在大道废弃、纯朴破灭以后才产生的。它们的产生，正说明了道德的破产、人心的堕落。
这是社会退步，而不是进步。
Benevolence and righteousness, knowledge and intelligence, filial piety and parental kindness, loyal ministers— these concepts all came about after the Dao was forsaken, after simplicity was destroyed. Their presence is an indication of moral bankruptcy, of the degeneration of people's hearts. They are evidence of a regression rather than a progression of society.

6

7

他才是我的忠臣！
This man is my only loyal minister!

绝学
Living With the Dao

学问知识是忧愁烦恼的根源,弃绝一切学问知识,就不会有忧愁烦恼。
Knowledge and learning are the root cause of distress. Forsake them, and you will free yourself of trouble and worry.

1

世人都趋荣避辱, 取善去恶, 但荣辱贵贱相差多少? 善与恶又相差多少?
People seek honor and avoid disgrace. They reach for goodness and shun badness. But is there really such a great difference between honor and disgrace? Between high and low? Between good and bad?

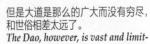

2

3

不过, 我也不能特立独行, 显露锋芒。大家畏惧的, 我也不能不畏惧。
Nevertheless, I can't exist entirely alone and make a showy display of my uniqueness. What other people fear, I must also fear.

4

但是大道是那么的广大而没有穷尽, 和世俗相差太远了。
The Dao, however, is vast and limitless. Oh, what a difference between it and the world in which we live.

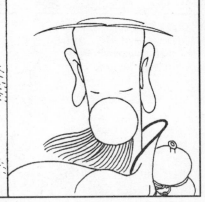

众人都兴高采烈的样子，好像参加丰盛的筵席，又像春天登台眺望景色。
唯独我恬淡无动于衷，好像不知嬉笑的婴儿。疲惫的样子，好像无家可归！
The masses look excited and happy, as if they were attending a feast or standing in a tower in the springtime looking out at an expansive view.
Only I am at peace in my calm sincerity, like an infant that has not yet learned to smile. I appear weary, as if I were homeless!

5

众人都有多余，唯独我好像不足的样子。我真是愚人的心肠啊！浑沌的样子。
The masses all have more than enough, and only I appear to be lacking. Oh, I am so foolish, as if I were muddled and confused.

6

世人都光耀自炫，唯独我昏昏昧昧的样子。
Everyone is so bright and dazzling, and only I appear obtuse and stupid.

7

世人都精明灵巧，唯独我无所识别的样子。
Everyone is so intelligent and talented, and only I appear completely undiscerning.

8

道
The Way

9

众人都好像很有作为，唯独我愚昧而笨拙。我和世人不同，而重视"道"的生活。
Everyone seems capable of doing so much, and only I appear foolish and inept. I am different from them — I live with the Dao.

贵、贱、善、恶、是、非、美、丑，这些价值判断并没有绝对性，只不过是相对形成的，经常随时代、环境而更改。世俗的人纵情于声、色、货、利。生活应该甘守淡泊，淡然无系，但求精神的提升。
High, low; good, bad; right, wrong; beautiful, ugly— these are mere value judgments rather than intrinsic qualities. They are relative and change according to the times and environment. People indulge so much in sound, sex, material things, and profit; but perhaps we should be happy in tranquillity, take pleasure in simplicity, and seek elevation of the spirit.

曲则全
Bend Don't Break

1
委曲可以保全；
To bend is to stay whole;

2
屈就反能伸展；
To flounder is to remain upright;

3
低洼得以充盈；
To lie low is to be filled up;

4
敝旧才能生新；
Only the old can be renewed;

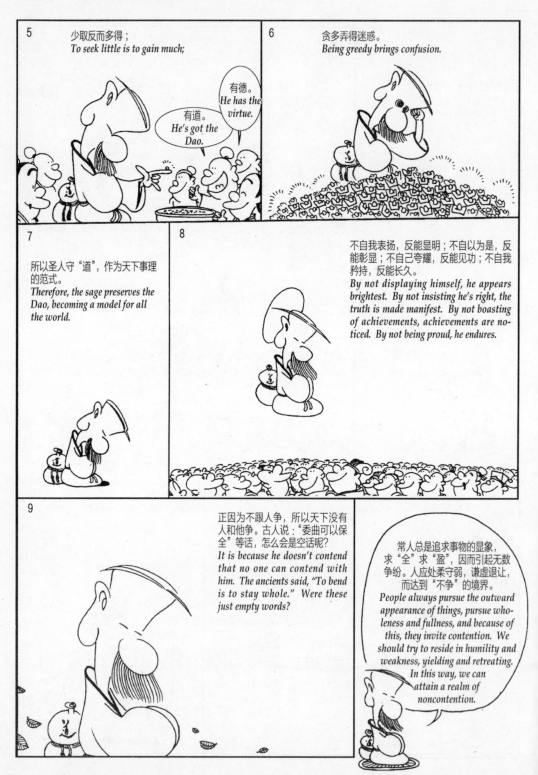

5
少取反而多得；
To seek little is to gain much;

有道。
He's got the Dao.

有德。
He has the virtue.

6
贪多弄得迷惑。
Being greedy brings confusion.

7
所以圣人守"道"，作为天下事理的范式。
Therefore, the sage preserves the Dao, becoming a model for all the world.

8

不自我表扬，反能显明；不自以为是，反能彰显；不自己夸耀，反能见功；不自我矜持，反能长久。
By not displaying himself, he appears brightest. By not insisting he's right, the truth is made manifest. By not boasting of achievements, achievements are noticed. By not being proud, he endures.

9
正因为不跟人争，所以天下没有人和他争。古人说："委曲可以保全"等话，怎么会是空话呢？
It is because he doesn't contend that no one can contend with him. The ancients said, "To bend is to stay whole." Were these just empty words?

常人总是追求事物的显象，求"全"求"盈"，因而引起无数争纷。人应处柔守弱，谦虚退让，而达到"不争"的境界。
People always pursue the outward appearance of things, pursue wholeness and fullness, and because of this, they invite contention. We should try to reside in humility and weakness, yielding and retreating. In this way, we can attain a realm of noncontention.

胜而不美
Victory Is Not Proud

锐利的兵器，是不祥的东西，大家都厌恶它。
Sharp weapons are instruments of misfortune, despised by all.

1

所以有"道"的人不使用它。
Those of the Dao keep their distance.

2

君子平时以左方为贵。
It's customary for the gentleman to seat an important person on the left.

3

右小！
Lowly on the right.

左大！
Great on the left.

4

右大！
Great on the right.

用兵时以右方为贵
In times of war, the important person is seated on the right.

左小！
Lowly on the left.

47

5 兵器是不祥的东西，不是君子所使用的东西。万不得已而使用它，最好要淡然处之。

Weapons are instruments of misfortune, something the gentleman does not use. If force is necessary, it is best to use it with reserve.

杀杀杀杀杀!
Kill! Kill !Kill!

胜利了也不要得意，如果得意，就是喜欢杀人，就不能在天下得到成功。

If you win, you must not be proud, because being proud would mean that you enjoy killing; and those who enjoy killing will not succeed in the world.

凶
Inauspicious

凶丧的事情以右方为上。
For inauspicious events, the right is honored.

吉
Auspicious

吉庆的事情以左方为上。
For auspicious events, the left is honored.

6

7 上将军在右方，用兵作战时候，偏将军在左方，这是把战争当作丧事来看待。

Seating the major general on the right and the lieutenant general on the left in time of war demonstrates that war is an inauspicious event.

左!
Left

右!
Right

8

丧
Funeral procession

杀人多了，要以悲哀的心情来悼念他们，即使打胜了，也要以丧事来处理。

Killing should be viewed with sorrow, and the dead should be grieved. Even a victory in war should be treated as a funeral.

武力带来凶灾祸害，用兵是不得已的事，应该心平气和，只求达到目的就好了。

Military force brings disaster, but sometimes there is no other alternative. In such a case, it should be carried out in a level-headed manner, seeking to attain the goal but no more.

自 知
Overcoming Yourself

能够了解别人优劣的，只能算是聪慧；
Understanding the good and the bad in other people is merely intelligence,

1

能够认识自己本心本性的，才可算是清明。
While understanding one's own nature is true enlightenment.

2

能够战胜别人的，可算是有力。
To be able to overcome others is to have power,Take that!

3

能够克服自己的，才算是坚强。
But to be able to overcome oneself is to have real strength.

我完了！我戒不了酒！
I'm finished!I'll can't stop drinking!

酒
Wine

能够知足而淡泊财物的，便可算是富有。
To be content without demanding too much is to be blessed with riches.

我很满意目前的生活。
I'm very pleased with my present life, thank you.

4 **5**

49

能够体道而强行不息的，便可算是有志。
One who can understand the Dao and perseveres in its application is a person of strong will.

道！
The Dao!

6

以道为本而紧守
One who can ta preserve it is on

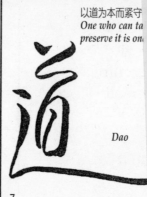

Dao

7

8

身虽死亡而精神不朽的，便可算是长寿。
And when he dies, his spirit will live forever. This is true longevity.

道
Dao

道
Dao

道
Dao

道
Dao

道
Dao

道
Dao

道
Dao

道
Dao

道
Dao

道
Dao

道
Dao

每一个人都有私、有欲，要想去私欲必须先自反自省，然后自清自虚。若能做到自知、自胜、知足和强行，那么就可以算是得道了。
Everyone is selfish and has desires. If we wish to rid ourselves of self-ish desires, we must first engage in self-examination, and then we must purify and empty ourselves. If we can understand ourselves, overcome ourselves, be content, and persevere, then we will have attained the Dao.

执"大道"
Holding
on to the Dao

执守大"道"，天下人都来归往。
If you can hold on to the Dao, the world will come to you.

1

归往而不互相伤害，于是大家都平和安泰。
If there is interaction without incident, then there will be peace among all.

2

3

音乐和美食能使过路人停步，
Good music and good food can halt a passerby.

4

但是"道"虽然淡而无味，看不见、听不到、却是使用不完。
The Dao is flavorless and silent. Although you cannot see it or hear it, it is inexhaustible in its usefulness.

仁义礼法之治，像音乐与美食一样，仅能满足人的耳目口腹之欲，道却能使人得到心灵的满足。
Government by benevolence, righteousness, propriety, and law is like the good music and good food, which only fulfill people's physical desires. The Dao fulfills our spiritual needs.

以柔克刚
The Strength of
Weakness

1

要收缩他，必定先使他扩张。
要削弱他，必先使他坚强。
要废弃他，必先提举他。
要套取他，必定先给予他。
To shrink something, first expand it.
To weaken something, first strengthen it.
To eliminate something, first glorify it.
To obtain something, first give something.

2

这是很明显的道理，柔弱一定
胜过刚强。
This is all so clear. Weakness
will always overcome
strength.

3

鱼不能离开渊，离开渊必定
干死。
If a fish leaves the depths, it
will die.

4

柔弱是治国的根本，治国
不用柔弱，必定灭亡。
Weakness is the foun-
dation of government,
and if it is not used, the
nation will be lost.

权谋、刑罚，都是凶利的东西，
不能够加施于人民。
Coercion and punishments are
evil means that must not be
used upon the people.

5

物极必反，势强必弱是千古不易的
道理。人君如果明白这个道理善加
运用，则能以柔克刚，以弱胜强了。
"Everything reverses direction
upon reaching its extreme" and
"The strong shall be weakened" are
ancient sayings. If you understand
and employ the principle behind
them, you, too, will be able to over-
come　　　　　strength with
*　　　　　　　weakness.*

第二部分：
Part II :

道

（下篇）

The Way

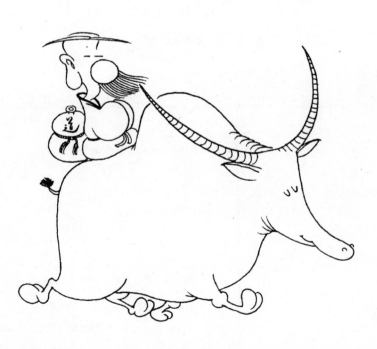

玄牝
The Mysterious Female

1 "道" 是永恒存在的，它能产生天地万物，所以称做 "玄牝"。
The Dao exists eternally. It is able to create the myriad things of the world and so is called "the mysterious female".

2 玄牝之门，就是天地的根源了。
The gate of the mysterious female is the source of the world.

道
Dao

3 它无形地存在着，永存不绝……
It exists invisibly and forever...

4 而它的作用，无尽无穷。
And its usefulness is inexhaustible.

无物
The Dao is Indistinct

看它看不见，叫做"夷"；
Something that is looked at but not seen is called invisible.

1

听它听不见，叫做"希"；
Something that is listened for but not heard is called inaudible.

2

因为道无色、无声、无形，所以它的形象无法穷究，是混沌一体的。
Because the Dao is invisible, inaudible, and intangible, it cannot be directly examined, and the three merge into one.

摸它摸不着，叫做"微"。
Something that is groped for but not found is called intangible.

3

4

它既不光亮，也不昏暗，渺茫难以形容，又回复到⋯⋯的状态……这叫⋯⋯
it is neither bright nor dark; it is vague and difficult to describe; it reverts to the formless. This is called the formless form. This is called indis-...

5

迎着它，看不见它的头；跟着它，又看不见它的尾……
...we do not see its head; following it, you do not see its tail...

Dao

6

能把握这亘古就已存在的道，就可以控驭现在的一切事物。能够知道原始的情形，就知道"道"的规律了。
If we are able to grasp the ancient Dao, we will be able to manage the things of the present. If we can understand the original conditions, we will understand the laws of the Dao.

7

"道"虽不可见、不可闻、不可搏，但确实是超越时空而存在。它虽然无形无象，但确是万事万物的主宰。
Although the Dao is invisible, inaudible, and intangible, it does indeed exist beyond time and space. Although it is without image or form, it is indeed the master of all things.

古之得"道"者
Daoists of Old

1

古时候得道的人，幽微、精妙、玄奥、通达，他的精神境界远超出一般人所能理解……

Daoists of the past were subtle, profound, mysterious, and perspicacious. They were far beyond what most people could comprehend...

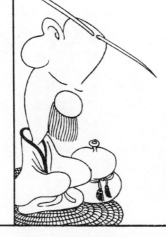

2

正因为他不是一般人所能理解，所以要勉强地把他描述一下……

And because they were beyond comprehension, the effort shall be made to describe them...

3

他立身行事，犹豫畏缩，就像冬天涉河一样，不敢贸然下水。

In his activities, such a person was cautious, as if crossing a river in winter.

4

他谨慎戒惧，就好像怕四邻窥伺一样。

He was alert and on his guard, as if fearful of threats form all sides.

57

他为人处世庄重拘谨，就像做客人一样。
In his behavior, he was dignified and courteous, as if a guest in someone's house.

他修道进德、除情去欲，就像春冰的融化一样。
He was also self-diminishing, like ice that has begun to melt.

5

6

他的本质敦厚朴实，就像未经雕琢的素材。
His character was simple and unaffected, like an uncarved medium.

他的胸怀宽广、态度谦下，就像幽深的山谷。
His outlook was expansive, and his attitude was one of lowliness, like a deep valley.

7

8

9

他的表现浑噩愚昧、不露锋芒，就像混浊的大水一样。
His outward expression made him appear mixed-up and foolish and was unrevealing of his abilities, like water that is turbid.

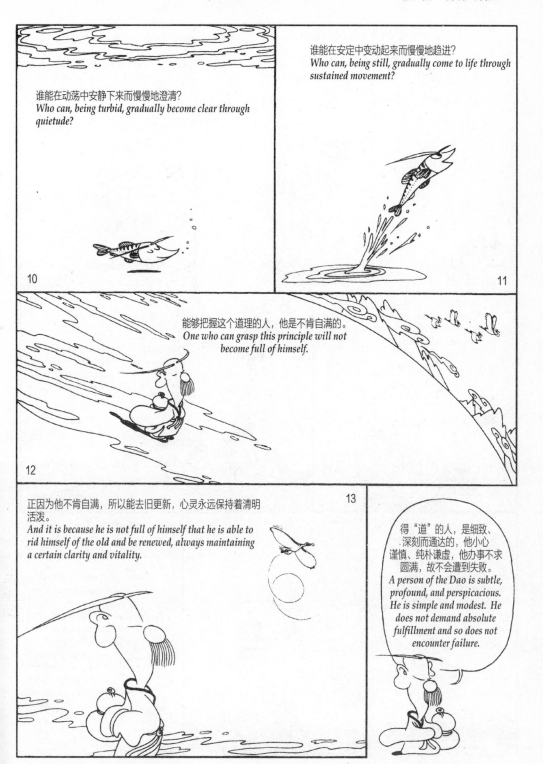

谁能在动荡中安静下来而慢慢地澄清？
Who can, being turbid, gradually become clear through quietude?

10

谁能在安定中变动起来而慢慢地趋进？
Who can, being still, gradually come to life through sustained movement?

11

能够把握这个道理的人，他是不肯自满的。
One who can grasp this principle will not become full of himself.

12

正因为他不肯自满，所以能去旧更新，心灵永远保持着清明活泼。
And it is because he is not full of himself that he is able to rid himself of the old and be renewed, always maintaining a certain clarity and vitality.

13

得"道"的人，是细致、深刻而通达的，他小心谨慎、纯朴谦虚，他办事不求圆满，故不会遭到失败。
A person of the Dao is subtle, profound, and perspicacious. He is simple and modest. He does not demand absolute fulfillment and so does not encounter failure.

绝圣弃智
The Artificial Role Model

1

抛弃了聪明和智慧，人民才有百倍的利益。

If you discard the concepts of sageliness and wisdom, the people will benefit a hundred-fold.

2

抛弃了仁和义，人民才能回到孝慈。

If you discard the concepts of benevolence and righteousness, the people will return to filial piety and parental compassion.

3

抛弃了巧和利，盗贼自然会绝迹。

If you discard the concepts of cleverness and profit, bandits and thieves will spontaneously disappear.

4

圣智
Sageliness and Wisdom

仁义
Benevolence and Righteousness

巧利
Cleverness and Profit

圣智、仁义、巧利，这三者都是文采罢了，是不足以治理天下的。

These three are mere adornments and insufficient to rule the land.

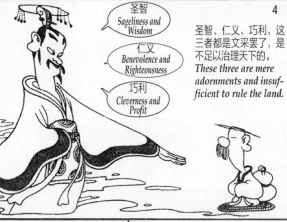

5

所以要使人民另外有所遵循，那便是：外表纯真，内心朴素，减少私心，降低欲望。

So give the people another pattern to follow: exhibit plainness, embrace simplicity, decrease selfishness, and reduce desires.

见素
Exhibit plainness

少私
Pecrease selfishness

抱朴
Harbor simplicity

寡欲
Reduce desires

圣智、仁义、巧利，都是人为，不仅不能为人类带来利益，反而会产生灾害；返璞归真，一切虚伪争夺就会自然消失。

Sageliness and wisdom, benevolence and righteousness, cleverness and profit—all of these are artificial, and not only are they not beneficial to mankind, they are actually harmful. If we return to simplicity and genuineness, all deceit and contention will naturally disappear.

道之为物
Reality of
the
Dao

1

有德之人的一行一动，都以"道"为准则。
In all actions, people of virtue take the Dao as their standard.

2

"道"这东西，说它是无又似乎有……
This thing the Dao is difficult to pin down. Sometimes it seems to not be there, and sometimes it does...

道 Dao

3

说它是实又似乎虚……
Sometimes it seems to be real, and sometimes it doesn't...

道 Dao

4

道 Dao

它是恍恍惚惚的，可是在恍惚之中，它又具备了宇宙形象；在恍惚之中，它又涵盖了天地万物。
It is vague and elusive, yet in this elusiveness it contains all the forms of the universe and includes all things throughout the world.

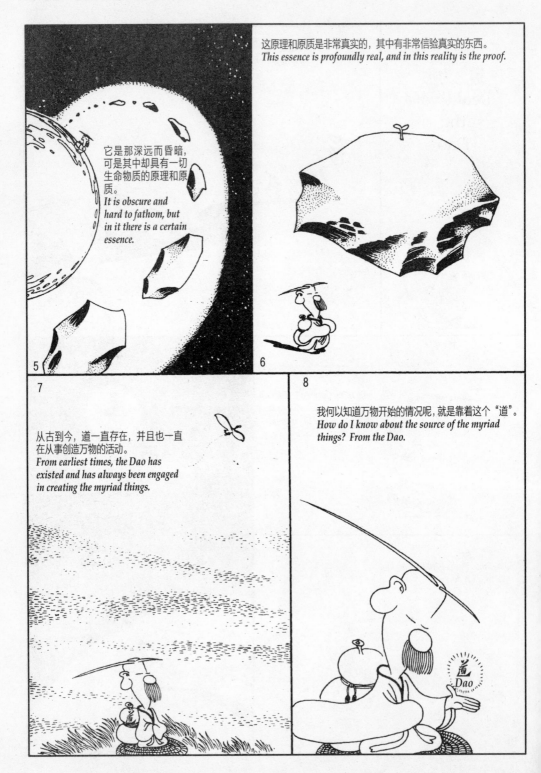

这原理和原质是非常真实的，其中有非常信验真实的东西。
This essence is profoundly real, and in this reality is the proof.

它是那深远而昏暗，可是其中却具有一切生命物质的原理和原质。
It is obscure and hard to fathom, but in it there is a certain essence.

5

6

7

从古到今，道一直存在，并且也一直在从事创造万物的活动。
From earliest times, the Dao has existed and has always been engaged in creating the myriad things.

8

我何以知道万物开始的情况呢，就是靠着这个"道"。
How do I know about the source of the myriad things? From the Dao.

道
Dao

希言自然
The Wanton Ruler

治理政事要无为而治，一切顺应自然。
Spareness of expression should be natural for a ruler.

1

所以狂风刮不了一早晨。
Just as wind storms don't outlast the morning...

2

暴雨下不了一整日。
And rainstorms don't outlast the day.

3

谁造成这样的情形呢？是天地。
天地造成的狂风暴雨尚且不能长久，何况人造成的苛刑虐政呢？
What causes these? Heaven and earth.
If even heaven and earth cannot persist, how can man?

4

所以从事于道的人，
就能得到道；
A person who works
with the Dao will
identify with the
Dao;

道
Dao

5

从事于德的人，就能得
到德；
A person who works
with virtue will iden-
tify with virtue.

德
Virtue

6

从事于不道不德的人，
就能得到不道不德。
A person who does
not work with the
Dao or virtue will
identify with neither
the Dao nor virtue.

7

得到道的人，道也乐于得到他；
For the person who identifies
with the Dao, the Dao gladly
takes him in;

Dao
道

8

企者不立
The Exhibitionist

抬起脚跟想要站得高的，反而站不牢；
One who stands on tiptoe hoping to gain stature cannot stand steady.

1

两步并作一步走的，反而快不了；
One who doubles his strides to get ahead cannot go faster;

2

3　专靠自己的眼睛看的，反而看不分明；
One who sees only with his own eyes does not see clearly;

瞧，我这文章写得多好！
Look, this essay of mine is fantastic!

不怎么样啊！
Not really!

4

自以为是的，反而判不清是非；
One who thinks he's always right is likely to make errors in judgement;

我的判断一定没错。
And there's no doubt in my mind that I'm correct.

错。
Wrong.

错。
Wrong.

66

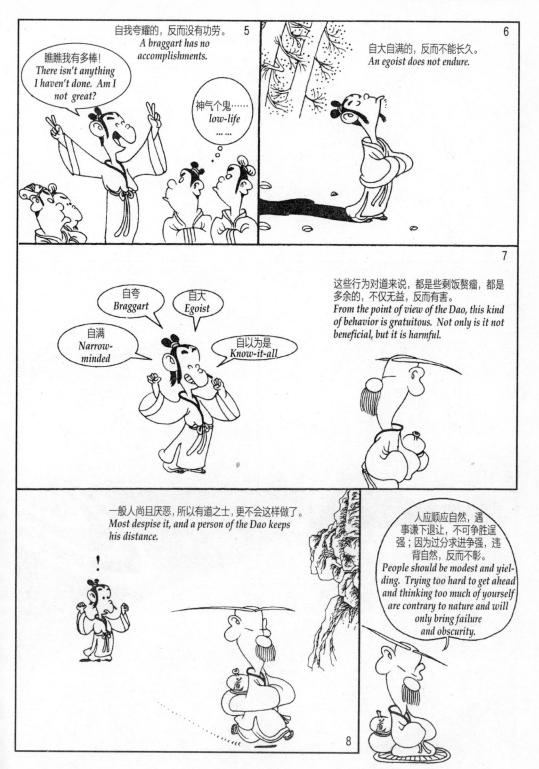

有物浑成
The Beginning

1 有一个浑然一体的东西，在天地还没有形成之前就已经存在了。

There was something formed from chaos, before the creation of heaven and earth.

2 它无声又无形。它永远不依靠外在的力量，不停地循环运行。

It is silent and formless. It stands alone always and never ceases coursing.

道
Dao

它可以算作天下万物的根本。我不知道它的名字，所以把它叫做"道"。

You could consider it the source of all things. I don't know what it's called, but if forced to name it, I would say "Dao".

3

勉强地描述它的形状，可说广大无边，广大无边就运行不息，运行不息就无远不达……

If forced to describe it, I would say "great". In its greatness, it courses; in its coursing, it travels far.

4

无远不达就返转还原，又返回到寂寥虚无。

Having traveled far, it returns to stillness and vacuity.

5

所以说:道大，天大，地大，人也大，宇宙间有四大，而人居其一。

So the Dao is great, Heaven is great, Earth is great, And people are also great. People are one of the four great things in the universe.

6

人以地为法则，地以天为法则，天以道为法则，道则以自然为法则。

People follow the earth, The earth follows heaven, Heaven follows the Dao, And the Dao follows spontaneity.

7

道生万物，万物无时不在变化，惟有道永恒不变，作用永不停止。道创生万物，并非有任何意图，只是顺应自然，听任万物的自化罢了，正因如此，道才能包举天地，纵贯古今，而为万物所推载。

The Dao produced the myriad things, which are ceaselessly changing. Only the Dao is eternal and constant, always functioning. The creation of the myriad things does not happen consciously, but is a spontaneous occurrence — the self-transformation of the myriad things by way of the Dao. In this way, the Dao envelops heaven and earth, endures the passage of time, and supports the myriad things.

处重守静
The Serious
Ruler

1 稳重为轻浮的根本。
Weightiness is the foundation of lightness.

轻
Light

重
Heavy

2 清净是急躁的主帅。
Quietude is the sovereign of frenzy.

静
Quiet

躁
Frenzied

3 所以体道的君子整天行走，却不离开辎重；
When traveling, a gentleman never strays far from the heavy wagons;

虽然有华丽的物质享受，却能泰然处之，不受它左右。
And even though in the lap of luxury, he resides tranquilly without being distracted by his surroundings.

一个万乘之国的君主，怎么可以轻浮急躁地来治理天下呢？
How could the ruler of a country a thousand miles across take ruling the country lightly or rule it with frenzy?

4

5

轻浮就失去了根本，急躁就不能清静了。
Taken lightly, a country will lose its foundation; ruled with frenzy, it will lose its sovereign.

6

重能御轻，静能制动，治理国家的人应该要处重守静，夷险一节，这样才能置国家于泰山之安。如果轻率将事，妄作妄为，必将身亡国灭了。
Weightiness controls lightness and quietude governs activity. In governing a country, one should maintain weightiness and quietude. If a ruler takes things lightly and acts recklessly, the country will be on the road to ruin.

善行无辙迹
Sagely Conservation

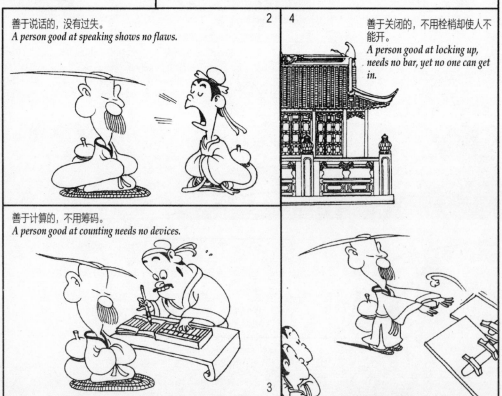

1

善于行走的，不留痕迹。
A person good at walking leaves no traces.

2

善于说话的，没有过失。
A person good at speaking shows no flaws.

4

善于关闭的，不用栓梢却使人不能开。
A person good at locking up, needs no bar, yet no one can get in.

善于计算的，不用筹码。
A person good at counting needs no devices.

3

善于捆缚的，不用绳索却使人不能解。
A person good at tying up needs no ropes, yet no one can get loose.

5

因此善人经常善于做到人尽其才，所以没有废弃的人；
Likewise, because a sage always gets the most out of people, no one is forsaken;

6

经常善于做到物尽其用，所以没有废弃的物。
And because he gets the most out of things, nothing is wasted.

7

能做到这些，真可说是得到道的精微高明了。
This is called profound understanding.

8

所以善人可以做不善人的老师，
A good person is the teacher of a person who is not good,

应该向他学习啊！
You should learn from him!

不善人可以做善人的借镜。
And a person who is not good is a mirror for a good person.

不能像他这样啊……
I shouldn't imitate him...

9

10

如果不善人不尊重善人……
If a person doesn't prize his teacher,

我为何要向他学习？
Why should I learn from him?

善人之珍视不善之人作为借镜……
Or take others as a mirror...

这种人最令人瞧不起了！
I can't stand such a person!

11

12

虽然自以为聪明，其实是大迷糊。这个道理真是奥妙啊！
Although he may think himself intelligent, he is actually confused. This is a subtle principle!

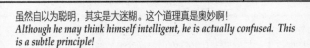

圣人顺任自然以待人接物，以无弃人无弃物的胸怀，对善人和不善人都能一律加以善待。
A sage treats people and things in accordance with nature, forsaking no one and wasting nothing. He is good to good and bad alike.

13

为天下谿
Confluence
of the World

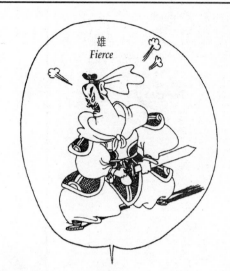

雄
Fierce

雌
Gentle

知道雄强的好处，而宁愿处在雌伏柔弱的地位，
To know the advantages of ferocity and yet keep to gentleness and pliancy,

1

2 **3**

这样才可作为天下的溪涧，使众流汇注。
Is to be the confluence of the world, with all the tributaries flowing to you.

作为天下的溪涧，常德就不会离失，而回复于自然的状态，就如同婴儿一样。
In being the confluence of the world, constant virtue will never leave you, and you will return to the naturalness of infancy.

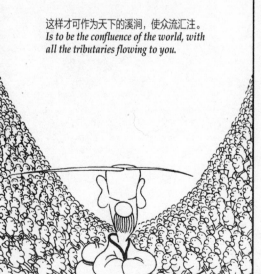

75

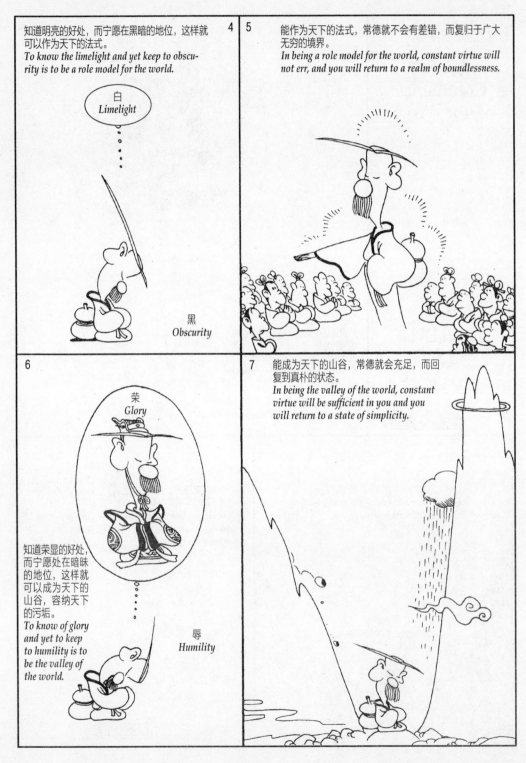

4 知道明亮的好处，而宁愿在黑暗的地位，这样就可以作为天下的法式。

To know the limelight and yet keep to obscurity is to be a role model for the world.

白
Limelight

黑
Obscurity

5 能作为天下的法式，常德就不会有差错，而复归于广大无穷的境界。

In being a role model for the world, constant virtue will not err, and you will return to a realm of boundlessness.

6 知道荣显的好处，而宁愿处在暗昧的地位，这样就可以成为天下的山谷，容纳天下的污垢。

To know of glory and yet to keep to humility is to be the valley of the world.

荣
Glory

辱
Humility

7 能成为天下的山谷，常德就会充足，而回复到真朴的状态。

In being the valley of the world, constant virtue will be sufficient in you and you will return to a state of simplicity.

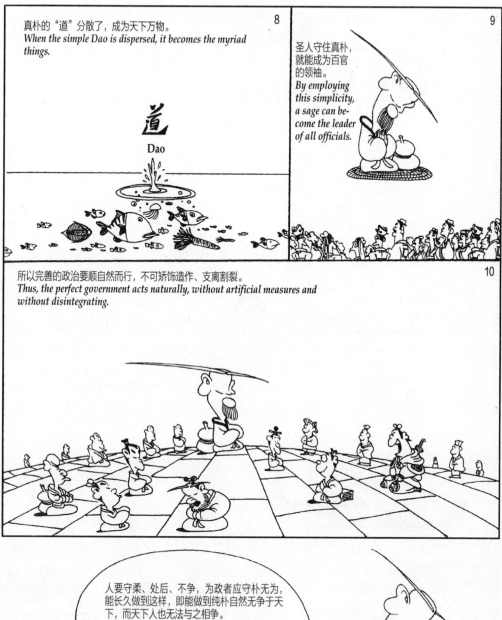

8

真朴的"道"分散了，成为天下万物。
When the simple Dao is dispersed, it becomes the myriad things.

道

Dao

9

圣人守住真朴，就能成为百官的领袖。
By employing this simplicity, a sage can become the leader of all officials.

10

所以完善的政治要顺自然而行，不可矫饰造作、支离割裂。
Thus, the perfect government acts naturally, without artificial measures and without disintegrating.

人要守柔、处后、不争，为政者应守朴无为，能长久做到这样，即能做到纯朴自然无争于天下，而天下人也无法与之相争。
If people keep to gentleness, humility, and non-contentiousness and if rulers keep to simplicity and non-action, no one will contend with them, and peace will reign.

欲取天下
A Natural Government

想要治理天下却用强力去做，我知道那是办不到的。

As for one who tries forcibly to govern the land, I don't think he would succeed.

1

2

天下是个很神妙的东西，治理它，不能强力而为、不能加以把持。强力而为的人必定败乱天下；

The world is a special place, and things can't be done too forcibly or with domination. A forceful person will fail in governing the land;

加以把持的人，必定失掉天下。

And a domineering person will lose the land.

3

人的禀性情状各有不同：有积极，有消极；有嘘暖，有吹寒；有刚强，有柔弱；有安定，有危险。
There are all different kinds of people in the world: some are active while others are passive, some are warm while others are cold, some are firm while others are soft, and some are stable while others are unsteady.

4

5

因此圣人治理天下，顺人情，依物势；
So in governing the land, a sage must act with respect to human nature and to circumstances;

6

必自然无为而治，而去除一切极端的、过分的措施。
He must govern through non-action and eliminate all extreme measures.

世间的物性不同，人性各别，为政者要能允许差异性与特殊性的发展，不可强行！理想的政治应顺任自然，因势利导，要舍弃一切过度的措施，去除一切酷烈的政举。
Everything in the world is different, including people, so a ruler must allow for the development of diversity and distinction and must not force things! The ideal government acts in accordance with nature, adjusting to circumstances, abandoning extreme measures, and eliminating harsh policies.

不矜不伐
War and Force

用"道"辅助君主的人，不靠兵力逞强于天下。
因为用兵服人，很容易引起报复。
A person who uses the Dao to assist the ruler does not coerce the people through force, as the situation can easily reverse.

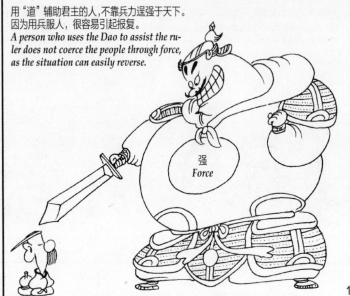

军队所到之处，荆棘就长满了。大战过后，一定会变成荒年。
Wherever the army goes, thorns and brambles spring up. After a great battle, there's sure to be a year of famine.

善用兵的人，只求用兵的目的达到就算了，不敢用兵力来逞强。
A good general works toward a specific goal then stops, not daring to force the situation.

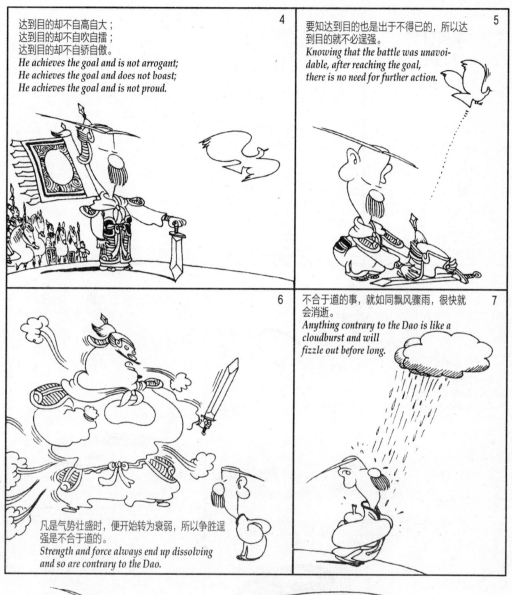

达到目的却不自高自大；
达到目的却不自吹自擂；
达到目的却不自骄自傲。

He achieves the goal and is not arrogant;
He achieves the goal and does not boast;
He achieves the goal and is not proud.

4

要知达到目的也是出于不得已的，所以达到目的就不必逞强。

Knowing that the battle was unavoidable, after reaching the goal, there is no need for further action.

5

凡是气势壮盛时，便开始转为衰弱，所以争胜逞强是不合于道的。

Strength and force always end up dissolving and so are contrary to the Dao.

6

不合于道的事，就如同飘风骤雨，很快就会消逝。

Anything contrary to the Dao is like a cloudburst and will fizzle out before long.

7

人类最愚昧最残酷的行为，莫过于战争这事。胜者也多是伤残累累。所以用兵应不矜不伐，处于不得已时才用兵，达到目的后就应自止。

Nothing humans do is more foolish or cruel than war. Even the victor is badly damaged. In warring, one should not be boastful or arrogant. The battle must be unavoidable, and when the objective met, action must be halted.

本诸自然
A Natural Balance

1

"道"永远是处于无名而朴实状态的，它虽然隐微，但是天下却没有人能够指使它。

The Dao is eternally nameless and simple. Though it seems small, nothing in the world can manipulate it.

2

侯王如果能抱守住它，万物都将自动归服。

If the kings and princes can keep it, all in the land will pay homage.

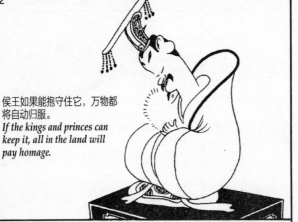

3

天地的阴阳二气相合，就降下甘露……

When the air of heaven and earth coalesce, sweet dew comes...

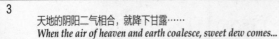

4

人们并不需要指使它、控制它，它就会很均匀。

It is all in balance, without people's interference.

5

道创造了万物，万物就有了名称。名称有了后，就应该知道适可而止。
There are names for everything created, but as soon as one starts using names, he must know to show restraint.

名
Fame

财
Money

位
Status

6

知道适可而止，才不会产生危险的事。
By knowing to show restraint, he can stay free from danger.

争利
I want profit!

争名
Give me fame!

7

道
Dao

道为天下所依归，就像江海百川的归宗，道也是万物的归趋。
Just as rivers return to the sea, so all things return to the Dao.

道生万物，本诸自然，万物各得
其养。治国的人如能效法天道顺应自然，
无欲无私，不造不设，万物自然各得其所，而无不服从。
The Dao created the myriad things, and all are nourished by nature. A ruler should emulate nature, with no desires or selfishness, no contriving or striving, and all will fall in line.

大道氾兮
The Dao Nurtures

大道流行泛溢，可左可右，无所不到。万物依赖它生长而不加主宰，成就了万物却不居功。

The Dao flows far and wide, able to go in all directions. The myriad things depend on it for life, yet it doesn't control them. It contributes greatly yet does not demand recognition.

养育了万物，却不主宰它们，可以说它很微小；

To nurture the myriad things without exerting mastery over them is to be known as small;

万物都归附于它而它不自以为主宰，又可以说它很伟大。

To have the myriad things pay allegiance to it and still not act exert mastery over them is to be known as great.

正因为它不自认为伟大，

It is its never seeing itself as great,

所以才能够成就它的伟大。

That proves its greatness.

道生长万物，养育万物，使万物各得所需、各适其性，而不加以主宰的精神，是统治者应学习的。

The Dao gives life to all things and nurtures all things. It allows all things to get what they need and to be themselves. It is its refusal to exert mastery over things that a ruler should emulate.

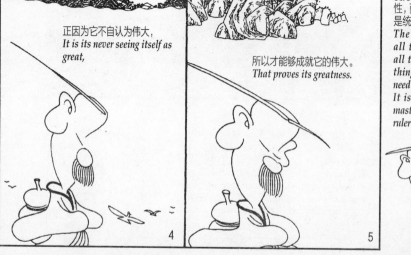

道常无为
The Natural
Ruler

道永远是顺应自然，好像是无所作为；
实际上是无所不为。
*The Dao always acts naturally and so
seems to do nothing. In fact, though,
nothing is left undone.*

1

2　侯王如能持守它，万物就会自生自长。
*If kings and princes can keep to it, the myriad things
will grow and transform on their own.*

3　自生自长而至贪欲萌作时，我就用道的真朴来镇服他。
*If desires arise from the growth and transformation,
we can subdue them through the na-
meless simplicity
of the Dao.*

朴
Simplicity

以道的真朴来镇服，万物就没有私欲而能清静，天下自然就会安定。
*By subduing them through the nameless simplicity of the Dao, the myriad things
will be free of selfish desires and will enjoy tranquillity, in which case there will
naturally be peace throughout the land.*

统治者应顺任自然，让人民自
我发展，要养成真朴的民风，
社会才能趋于安定。
*A ruler should follow nature,
and allow the people to develop on their own. If he can
cultivate an air of
simplicity among
the people, he can
create peace and
stability.*

4

第三部分：
Part Ⅲ :

德

（上篇）

The Virtue

上德无为
Superior Virtue Is Not Virtue

Panel 5:
上"礼"的人有所作为，若得不到回应……
People of superior propriety act, and if ignored...

礼!
Proper!

Panel 6:
无"礼"的家伙!
Cad!

于是就伸出手臂来使人们强从。
Reach their hand out and force you to respond.

Panel 7:
所以失去了"道"，而后才有"德"；失去了"德"，然后才有"仁"；失去了"仁"，而后才有"义"；失去了"义"，而后才有"礼"。
So with the loss of the Dao, "Virtue" arose; with the loss of virtue, "benevlence" arose; with the loss of benevolence, "righteousness" arose; with the loss of righteousness, "propriety" arose.

道!
Dao!

德!
Virtue!

仁!
Benevolence!

义!
Righteousness!

礼!
Propriety!

Panel 8:
当社会需要用"礼"维系的时候，虚伪巧诈也就产生了，祸乱就跟着来了。
When society needs the restraints of propriety, hypocrisy and fraud arise, with disaster following right on their heels.

Panel 9:
自以为聪明的人，以智取巧，实在是愚昧的根源。
Presuming to be knowledgeable and putting your knowledge to cunning usefulness is the source of foolishness.

Panel 10:
因此大夫应守质朴的大道，不要虚伪的巧智。舍弃礼智的浮华，取用道的厚实。
You should maintain the simplicity of the Dao, and not be crafty or hypocritical. Do away with the superficiality of propriety and knowledge, and employ instead the genuineness of the Dao.

道德修养共分道、德、仁、义、礼、智。合于道的社会，一切需自然而行，当社会需要礼智来维系时，诈伪丛生，已经是不堪设想的时候了。
The elements of morality are virtue, benevolence, righteousness, propriety, and knowledge. In a society that is in accord with the Dao, all things proceed according to nature. When the Dao is forsaken, society breaks down and needs the restraints of these moral elements to keep it together.

有生于无
Getting So-mething From Nothing

1

道的运行反复循环，周流不息，才能产生绵延不尽的生命。
The Dao moves in cycles over and over, flowing unceasingly, and in this way, gives rise to the endless flourishing of life.

2

道的作用柔弱谦下。
The functioning of the Dao is weak and humble.

3

天下万物是从"有"而产生的，
The myriad things under heaven are generated from Being.

有
Being

4

而"有"却是从"无"产生的。
And Being arises from Nothing.

无
Nothing

"无"是道之体，"有"是道之用，人应无为、无事、无智、知知、无欲、无我、无私，才能达到"道"的最高境界。
Nothing is the substance of the Dao, and Being is its function. In order to achieve the realm of the Dao, we must first reconcile ourselves with non-action, not engaging in affairs of the world, non-intellectualizing, no-knowledge, no-desires, egolessness, and selflessness.

道生万物
Universal Harmony

道是万物创生的总原理，万物创生的程序是由道生出一种气。
The Dao is the underlying principle behind the creation of the myriad things. The order of the process giving rise to the myriad things began with the Dao producing a kind of generative force.

道
Dao

1

这种气又化分成为阴阳两气。
This force gave rise to the two forces of the Yin and Yang.

2

3

阴阳两气相交，而成一种适匀的状态……
The interaction of the Yin and Yang led to a state of dynamic balance...

4

于是万物都在这种状态中产生了。
From which the myriad things issued forth.

5

万物都背阴而向阳，阴阳两气互相激荡，而成新的和谐体。
The myriad things have their backs to the Yin and face the Yang. Through the blending of the Yin and Yang, a new harmony is created.

"道"创生了万物，万物创生以后，还要守住道的精神，依道而行。应该柔弱，应该顺应自然。
The Dao created the myriad things, and after their creation, they must still preserve the spirit of the Dao and act in harmony with the Dao. We, too, should be yielding and act in accordance with nature.

至 柔
Soft Will
Overcome

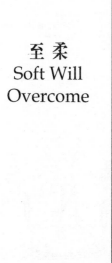

1

天下最柔软的东西，能驾御天下最坚硬的东西。
The softest things can overcome the hardest things.

2

无形的力量能穿透没有间隙的东西。
The formless can penetrate the solid.

3

我因此知道"无为"的益处。
This is how I know of the advantage of non-action.

4

"不言"的教导，"无为"的益处，天下少有比得上的。
Nothing is better than the wordless teaching and the advantage of non-action.

水是最柔不过的，却能穿山透地。柔能胜刚是很明显的道理啊！

Water is the most pliant of all things, and yet it can carve out mountains and penetrate the ground. That the weak will overcome the firm is so clear.

知足不辱
The Risk of Seeking Fame and Fortune

1

名和生命比起来哪一样亲切？
Which do you hold more dear, fame or life?

声名
Fame

生命
Life

2

生命和货利比起来哪一样贵重？
Which do you value more, life or wealth?

货利
Wealth

生命
life

3

得到名利和丧失生命哪一样为害？
Which is more harmful, gaining fame and fortune, or losing you life?

名利
Fame and fortune

4

奖
First Prize

名人
Cele-brity

赏
Award

冠军
Cham-pion

因此过分地爱名，就必定要付重大的耗费。
There is a high price to pay in seeking fame.

5

藏财货太多，就必定会招致惨重的损失。
Hoarding wealth will inevitably bring heavy losses.

知道满足就不会受到屈辱，知道适可而止就不会带来危险。
Understanding contentment will not elicit insults. Knowing when to stop will not bring danger.

6

人应爱惜身体、生命，不应过分追求名利，得到名利而失去生命，是得不偿失的。
We should cherish our body and our life. Is it really worth it to seek fame and fortune at the risk of losing your life?

欲 得
There Is No Greater Crime

天下有道的时候，人人知足知止，国与国之间和平相处。
When the Dao is in the world, people are content and easily satisfied and countries get along peacefully.

战争绝迹了，战马也没有用了，只好用来耕田。
There are no wars, so horses once used for battle are used to till the fields.

天下无道的时候，人人逐利争名。
When the Dao is absent from the world, people contend for fame and wealth.

国与国之间战争不断，所有的马都用来作战，母马都得在战场上生产。
Countries fight continuously, and all horses are used for battle, even mares must give birth on the battlefield.

万事万物的原理，并不在远不可及的地方，它就在我们的心中。

The answer to the mystery of all things doesn't lie in some far off land but is right in our own hearts.

1

不行而知
Don't Go Out

2

若能内观反省，除私去欲，不出门外就能知天下的事理，不望窗外就可明了自然的法则。

If you can examine your inner self, banishing selfishness and forsaking desire, you will be able to understand the principles behind all things without taking one step outside your door; you will comprehend the laws of nature without so much as looking out your window.

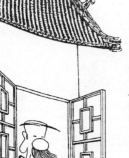

3

走出大门愈远，知道的事理也就愈少。

The further you go from home, the less you will understand.

4

所以圣人不外出远求，天下的事理就可以明了。

So the sage understands without journeying,

5

不造作施为，万物就可以化育生成。

Does not act unnaturally, and the myriad things flourish effortlessly.

心灵深处是透明的，像一面镜子，应净化欲念，清除心灵的蔽障，去了解外物。

Our souls are transparent, like mirrors. Through judiciously wiping away the blemishes on our souls, we will naturally come to understand the things around us.

无 为
In Pursuit
of
Non-action

求"学"一天比一天增加，
When pursuing knowledge, you will experience a daily increase.

我的知识见闻增加了不少。
Wow, I've learned so much!

求"道"却一天比一天减少，减少又减少，一直到无为的境地。
But when pursuing the Dao, you will experience a daily decrease— less and less every day, until you arrive at the realm of non-action.

情欲减少了！
Wow, my desires have decreased so much!

如能不妄为，那就没有什么事情做不成了。
Through taking no unnecessary action, anything can be accomplished.

1

2

3

第二点规定……
The second rule is...

第三点规定……
The third rule is...

第四点规定……
The fourth rule is...

第一点规定……
The first rule is...

治理国家要常清静、不扰攘，至于政举繁苛，就不配治理国家了。
Governing a country requires tranquillity rather than interference in the people's affairs.

"为学"，只能增知添欲，因此虚伪百出、忧烦丛生。
"求道"，损知去欲，内心既清且虚，外在自然无为无事了。
Pursuing knowledge serves only to increase our desires, thus creating hypocrisy and causing frustration. Pursuing the Dao eliminates intellectualizing and decreases desires. On the inside you will be pure and empty, and on the outside you will naturally adhere to non-action and not engage in worldly affairs.

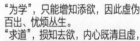

4

圣人
The Ideal Leader

"圣人"没有成见，以百姓的意见为意见。
The sage holds no prejudice. He takes the people's opinion as his own.

1

善良的人，我善待他；不善良的人我也善待他。这样可使人人向善。
I am good to good people and bad people, alike. In this way, I can cause the people to be good.

善!
Good!

2

守信的人我善待他；不守信的人，我也善待他。这样可使人人守信向善。
I trust trustworthy people, and I trust untrustworthy people. In this way, I can cause the people to be trustworthy.

信!
Trustworthy!

3

"圣人"在位，收敛自己的意欲，使人心思化归于浑朴，百姓都凝视静听，如痴如愚，圣人都把他们当作婴儿一样的爱护。
When a sage is governing, he restrains his desires, making the people simple and innocent. The people stare and listen quietly, as though ignorant or dumb. The sage protects them as he would infants.

4

理想的治者，收敛自我的意欲，不以主观厘定是非好恶的标准，应以善心诚心去对待所有的老百姓。
The ideal ruler restrains his desires, doesn't codify his own subjective standards of right and wrong, and treats all people with goodness and sincerity.

97

兕 虎
A Tiger May
Be Vicious

人出生后，能够长寿的，有十分之三。
Of all people born, one third live long, healthy lives;

短命夭折的有十分之三。
One third die prematurely;

本来可以长寿，而自己走进死路的，也有十分之三。
And one third would have lived long lives, but cause their own premature deaths.

这是什么原因呢？
Why is this?

2

因为奉养太厚、享受太过了。
Because they over-indulge in pleasure and spoil themselves.

3

99

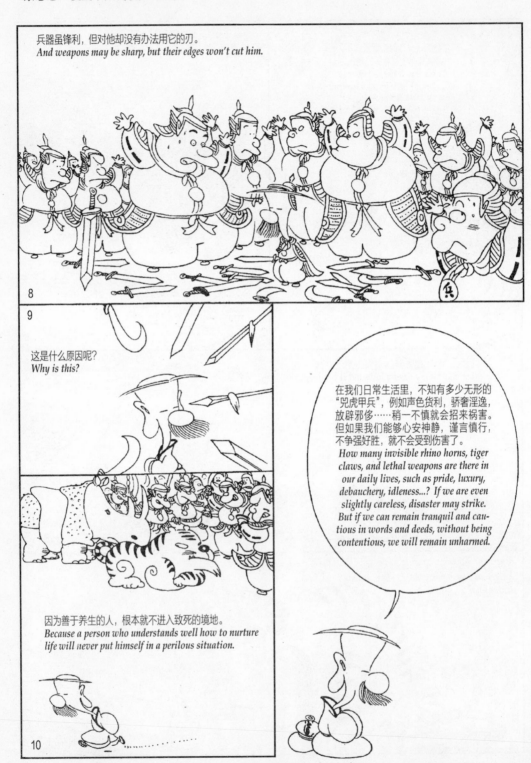

兵器虽锋利，但对他却没有办法用它的刃。
And weapons may be sharp, but their edges won't cut him.

8

9

这是什么原因呢？
Why is this?

在我们日常生活里，不知有多少无形的"兕虎甲兵"，例如声色货利，骄奢淫逸，放辟邪侈……稍一不慎就会招来祸害。但如果我们能够心安神静，谨言慎行，不争强好胜，就不会受到伤害了。
How many invisible rhino horns, tiger claws, and lethal weapons are there in our daily lives, such as pride, luxury, debauchery, idleness...? If we are even slightly careless, disaster may strike. But if we can remain tranquil and cautious in words and deeds, without being contentious, we will remain unharmed.

因为善于养生的人，根本就不进入致死的境地。
Because a person who understands well how to nurture life will never put himself in a perilous situation.

10

玄同
One Who Speaks
Does Not Know

智者晓得道体精微奥妙，所以勤而行之，不敢多言。
A wise person understands the subtlety and mystery of the Dao and so cautiously puts it into practice, not daring to be too talkative.

1

成天喋喋不休的人，根本不晓得"道"。
Those who prattle on and on understand nothing about the Dao.

2

不露锋芒，消解纷扰；含敛光耀，混同尘世；这就是玄妙齐同的境界。
Do not reveal your sharpness; eliminate all complications; withhold your brightness; merge with the dusty world. This is the realm of mysterious identity.

完全超然物外，淡泊无欲，既无法和他亲近，也无法和他疏远，既无法使他得利，也无法使他受害，既无法使他高贵，也无法使他低贱。修养到达这种境界，才是天下最了不起的人。
By transcending the material world and being tranquil, no one can get too close to you, no one can alienate you, no one can benefit you, no one can harm you, no one can honor you, and no one can debase you. This is the highest realm that can be attained by any person.

理想的人格形态是"挫锐""解纷""和光""同尘"，而到达"玄同"的最高境界。
By being humble and untroubled, we control our own circumstances, and no one else can make or break us.

3　　4

无欲自朴
The More Laws
There Are...

1

以清静之道治国。
Govern through tranquillity.

奇 Special Forces　　奇 Special Forces

SpeciForces

以诡奇的方法用兵。
Be cunning in war.

2

3

以不搅扰人民来治理天下。
Win over the whole land through non-interference.

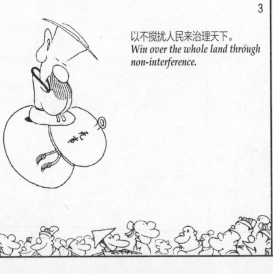

4

我怎么会知道是这样的? 从下面这些事端上可以看出来：
How do I know this? From the following:

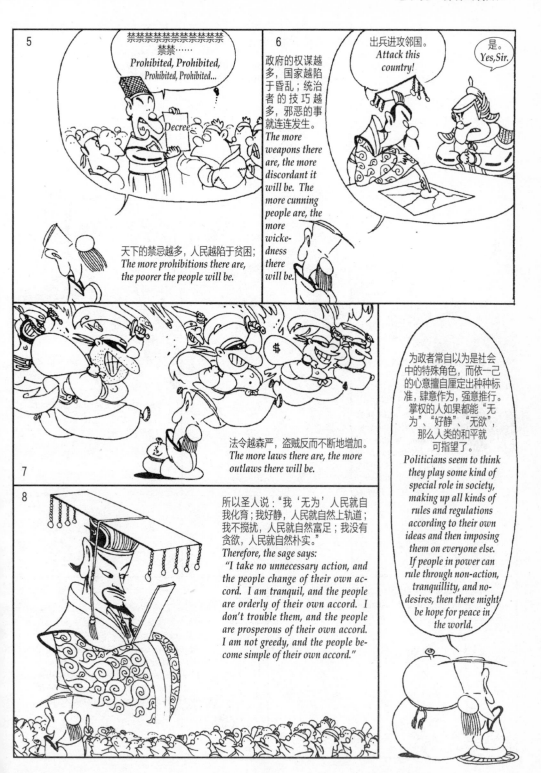

5

禁禁禁禁禁禁禁禁禁禁禁
禁禁……
Prohibited, Prohibited,
Prohibited, Prohibited...

Decree

天下的禁忌越多，人民越陷于贫困；
The more prohibitions there are,
the poorer the people will be.

6

政府的权谋越多，国家越陷于昏乱；统治者的技巧越多，邪恶的事就连连发生。
The more weapons there are, the more discordant it will be. The more cunning people are, the more wickedness there will be.

出兵进攻邻国。
Attack this country!

是。
Yes, Sir.

7

法令越森严，盗贼反而不断地增加。
The more laws there are, the more outlaws there will be.

为政者常自以为是社会中的特殊角色，而依一己的心意擅自厘定出种种标准，肆意作为，强意推行。掌权的人如果都能"无为"、"好静"、"无欲"，那么人类的和平就可指望了。
Politicians seem to think they play some kind of special role in society, making up all kinds of rules and regulations according to their own ideas and then imposing them on everyone else. If people in power can rule through non-action, tranquillity, and no-desires, then there might be hope for peace in the world.

8

所以圣人说："我'无为'人民就自我化育；我好静，人民就自然上轨道；我不搅扰，人民就自然富足；我没有贪欲，人民就自然朴实。"
Therefore, the sage says:
"I take no unnecessary action, and the people change of their own accord. I am tranquil, and the people are orderly of their own accord. I don't trouble them, and the people are prosperous of their own accord. I am not greedy, and the people become simple of their own accord."

烹小鲜
Frying Fish

1
治理大国好像煎小鱼一样，不能常常翻动。
Governing a large country is like frying a small fish, you can't turn it over too often.

2
翻动太多，小鱼就破碎了。
If turned over too many times, the fish will fall apart.

3
用清静无为的道理治理天下，天神人鬼都能各安其位。所以鬼不会作祟害人，
By governing through tranquillity and non-action, the gods and spirits remain in their proper places. So the spirits do not harm people,

4
神也不会伤害人。
And neither do the gods.

5
圣人也不会伤害人。
Sages also do not harm the people.

6
在上位的国君和在下位的人民互相都不伤害，于是天下太平。
If the ruler and the people do not harm each other, there will be peace throughout the land.

为政之要在安静无扰，若能"清静无为"，则人人便可各遂其生，而相安无事。
If a ruler can lead through tranquillity and not interfere with the lives of the people, if the ruler can maintain serenity and non-action, then the people can go about their own lives and be peaceful and prosperous of themselves.

乐 推
Navigating
the State

1

江海所以能成为百川之王，使所有的河流奔注，是因为它善于自处低下的地位。

The ocean is the king of all rivers and causes them all to come running into itself because it skillfully stays below them.

2

所以"圣人"要作为人民的领导，必须对他们谦下。

So in leading the people, a sage must also put himself below. To be ahead of the people, he must put himself behind them.

3

所以"圣人"居于上位而人民不感到负累，居于前面而人民不感到受害。所以人民乐于推戴而不厌弃。

Therefore, while the sage resides above the people, the people do not feel burdened, and with him at the front, the people do not feel threatened. In this way, the people will gladly support and respect their leader and not loathe and forsake him.

4

因为他不跟人争，所以天下没有人能和他争。

Because he does not contend, no one can contend with him.

统治者权势在握，一旦肆意妄作，人民就不堪其累了；因此应尽量避免带给人民负担与累害。

If a leader takes advantage of his power, he is taking advantage of the people. A good leader remembers that he is a servant of the people.

不争
The Good General

善作将帅的，不逞勇武。善于作战的，不轻易激怒。
A good general is not excessively violent. A good soldier is not easily angered.

1

2　善于战胜敌人的，不用对斗。
A good conqueror does not resort to confrontation.

不！不用打他们自然崩败。
No need, they'll fall apart of their own accord.

将军，与他们拼了！
Let's go for it, General!

善于用人的，对人谦下。
One who is good at employing others puts himself below them.

3

这"不武"、"不怒"就是不和人争胜斗气的道德。
This kind of non-violence and even-temper is known as the virtue of noncontention.

如果能做到这些，便是符合自然的道理。
If you can accomplish the above, you will be living in accordance with the principles of nature.

"武"、"怒"是侵略的行为，"不武"、"不怒"、不逞强、不暴戾，最合于自然的道理。
Violence and anger are acts of aggression, while nonviolence and an even-temper match best the principles of nature.

4

5

知 知
The
Know-it-all

Panel 1

能知道自己有所不知道, 这是最高明的了。
It is best to recognize what you do not know.

抱歉! 这方面的知识我不懂。
I'm sorry, but I'm not familiar with that subject.

1

Panel 2

不知道却自以为知道, 这就是缺点。
To not realize your ignorance is a definite defect.

我懂得很多, 什么都懂, 诗、书、画无一不精。
I understand everything—poetry, calligraphy, painting... you name it, I know it.

其实什么都只知皮毛。
Superficially at best.

2

Panel 3

圣人没有这个缺点, 因为圣人厌恶这个缺点, 所以才没有这个缺点。
Therefore, the reason a sage is without defect is that he recognizes defects as such.

Ha! Ha!

3

Panel 4

有的人只看到事物的表层, 一知半解就以为自己都懂了。知道自己愚蠢, 是智者, 不知道自己愚蠢, 才是真正的愚蠢。
Some people see only the surface of things, and with just a little knowledge they think they understand it all. It is the wise person who recognizes his ignorance. And it is the person who doesn't know he is ignorant who is the real fool.

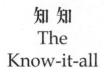

不争善胜
Contend
By
Not Contending

勇于表现刚强，就会送命。
One who is brave in firmness will die.

2

勇于表现柔弱，反能生存。
One who is brave in pliancy, however, will survive.

3

这两种同样是勇敢，但勇于柔弱就有利，勇于刚强就有害。
These are both bravery, but one is beneficial while the other is harmful.

天为什么厌恶"勇于敢"？有谁知道是什么原因？

Why does heaven dislike "bravery in firmness"? Who knows the reason?

自然的规律是不争攘而善于得胜，不说话而善于回应，不召唤而万物自动归附，宽广坦荡而善于筹策。

The way of nature is to win without contending, to reply without speaking, to have things come without calling, to plan without worrying.

自然的范围广大无边，像一张大网一样，笼罩的范围无所不包，它虽稀疏，却从来没有一点漏失。

Nature is vast, like a giant net that covers everything, and although the meshes are wide, nothing slips through them.

自然的规律是柔弱不争的。人类的行为应效法自然的规律，而恶戒刚强好斗。

The laws of nature are pliant and noncontending. We should take nature as our example and dispense with firmness and contention.

草 木
Tree vs. Grass

1

人活着时，身体是柔软的，死了的时候就变僵硬了。
When people are alive, their bodies are tender and soft. When dead, they become stiff and hard.

2

草木生长的时候是柔脆的，
Plants are also tender and supple when alive,

3

死了的时候就变干枯了。
Only to become dry and brittle when they die.

4

所以坚强的东西属于死亡的一类，
Stiff and hard things belong to the realm of the dead,

5

柔弱的东西属于生存的一类。
While the tender and soft belong to the realm of the living.

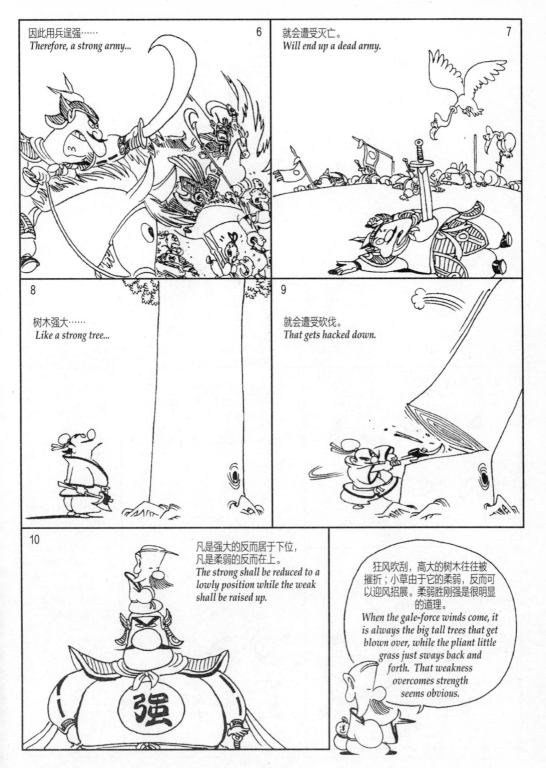

6
因此用兵逞强……
Therefore, a strong army...

7
就会遭受灭亡。
Will end up a dead army.

8
树木强大……
Like a strong tree...

9
就会遭受砍伐。
That gets hacked down.

10
凡是强大的反而居于下位，
凡是柔弱的反而在上。
*The strong shall be reduced to a
lowly position while the weak
shall be raised up.*

强

狂风吹刮，高大的树木往往被
摧折；小草由于它的柔弱，反而可
以迎风招展。柔弱胜刚强是很明显
的道理。
*When the gale-force winds come, it
is always the big tall trees that get
blown over, while the pliant little
grass just sways back and
forth. That weakness
overcomes strength
seems obvious.*

111

水 石
Water vs. Rock

1

世间没有比水更柔弱的，
Nothing is more pliant than water,

2

可是它却有攻坚克强的能力。
And nothing can attack hard and strong things better.

弱胜过强，柔胜过刚，天下没有人不知道，但是没有人能实行。
The weak overcomes the strong, the soft overcomes the hard. Everyone knows this, but no one is able to put it into practice.

3

4

因此圣人说：“承担全国的屈辱，才配称社会的君主；承担全国的祸难，才配做国家的君王。”
So the sage says, "Only the person who can shoulder the disgraces and disasters of a country is fit to be its leader."

水性柔弱，而无坚不摧，无强不克，柔弱却含有无坚不克的性格，而胜过刚强。
The nature of water is pliancy, and yet there is no firmness it can't penetrate and no strength it can't overcome. Maybe we can learn something from water.

予而不取
It's Better to Give Than to Receive

1

重大的仇怨，纵使把它调解，也会有余怨藏在心底。这怎能算是妥善的办法呢？

After a bitter feud, it is difficult to adjust, and some bad feelings are bound to remain. How can this be a satisfactory conclusion?

你不对！
You're wrong!

不要再争执了！
Stop fighting!

你错！
Am not!

2

因此"圣人"保存借据，只给予人而不向人索取偿还。

Therefore, a sage may loan money, and though he keeps the promissory note, he will not exact repayment.

3 有德的人对待人，就像持有借据的人那样，只给予人而不索取。

A person of virtue treats oth-ers like the person patiently holding the promissory note. He gives but does not take.

O.U.

4 无德的人，对待就像税吏，只向人索取，而不给人家。

A person without virtue, on the other hand, treats other people as if he were a tax collector — only taking and never giving.

税
Taxes

天道是无所偏私的，经常帮助好人。

Like the proverb says: The heavenly Dao is impartial — it is always with good people.

为政者不可蓄怨于民，用税赋来榨取百姓，用刑政来钳制大家。理想的政治是以"德"化民，辅助人民，给予而不索取，绝不骚扰百姓。

Leaders should not breed contempt in the people. They should never exploit the people through severe taxes or use force to coerce them. The ideal government transforms the people through virtue. It assists the people by giving and not taking and never harasses them.

5

圣人不积
The More You
Give, the More
You Get

真实的话不好听，
True words are not pleasant to hear;

1

好听的话不真实。
Words that are pleasant to hear are not true.

2

行为良善的人不巧辩，
A good person does not argue,

3

巧辩的人不良善。
An argumentative person is not good.

4

真正了解的人，晓得宇宙间的大道就在自己心中，不必广心博骛。
A wise person understands that the great Dao of the universe lies within one's own heart and that it isn't necessary to run around in search of it.

5

知识广博的人，未必对大道有真知。
A person of broad knowledge doesn't necessarily understand the great Dao.

6

圣人没有私心，什么都无所保留，他尽量帮助别人，自己反而更充足。
The sage is unselfish, keeping nothing for himself. The more he helps others, the more he gains.

7

倾其所有给予别人，自己反而更富有。
天道无私，只有利于万物，而不会对万物造成伤害。
The more he gives to others, the more he has.
The heavenly Dao is not selfish. It only benefits the myriad things and does not harm them.

8

圣人顺天道而行，只是贡献施与，而不和人家争夺。
The sage acts in accordance with the Dao, providing without contending.

9

圣人能效法"利而不害"的天道，而表现"为而不争"。结果"天下莫能与之争"。"施者比受者有福"，能不和人争夺功名的精神，就是一种伟大的道德行为。
The sage "helps without harming" and "acts without contending". As a result, "Nothing and no one can contend with him". The saying, "To give is better than to receive" demonstrates this noncontentious spirit and exhibits, as well, the spirit of the Dao.

第四部分：
Part Ⅳ :

德

（下篇）

The Virtue

得一者
Obtaining the One

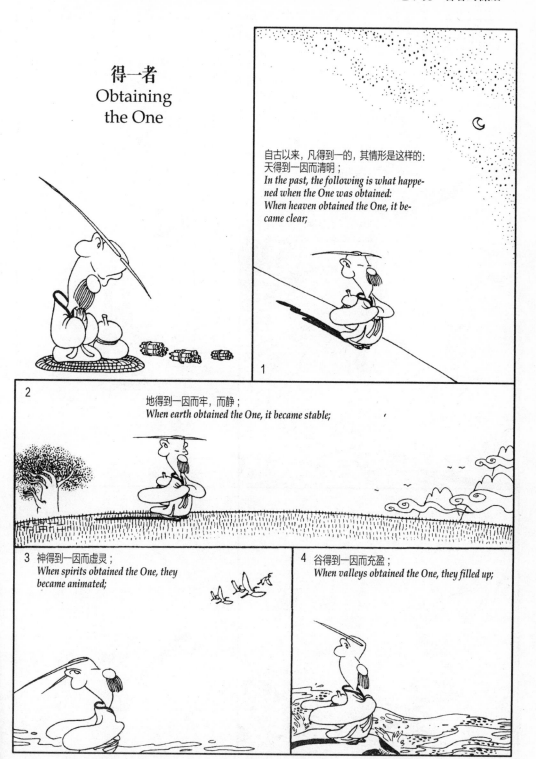

自古以来，凡得到一的，其情形是这样的：
天得到一因而清明；
In the past, the following is what happened when the One was obtained:
When heaven obtained the One, it became clear;

1

2
地得到一因而牢，而静；
When earth obtained the One, it became stable;

3 神得到一因而虚灵；
When spirits obtained the One, they became animated;

4 谷得到一因而充盈；
When valleys obtained the One, they filled up;

5　万物得到一因而化生；
When the myriad things obtained the One, they came to life;

7　侯王得到一因而使天下安定。这些都是由于得到一才有的。
When kings and princes obtained the One, the land became ordered. These all happened because the One was obtained.

6　天不能清明，恐怕就要崩塌；
If heaven is not clear, it may crack wide open;

8　地不能宁静，恐怕就要覆灭；
If the earth is not stable, it may crumble;

9　神不能虚灵，恐怕就要消失；
If spirits are not animated, they may pass away;

10
谷不能充盈，
恐怕就要枯竭；
If valleys are not filled up, they may go bone dry;

11　万物不能生长，恐怕就要灭绝；
If the myriad things do not come to life, they may go extinct;

12　侯王不能成为天下典范标准，恐怕就要颠覆灭亡。
And if kings and princes do not put the land in order, they may be toppled.

13　贵以贱作为根本，
The valuable takes the base as its root,

14　高以下作为基础。
And the high takes the low as its foundation.

因此，侯王们自称"孤"、"寡"、"不穀"，以示谦下，这不是贵以贱为根本吗？岂不是吗？

It is for this reason that kings and princes refer to themselves as "the orphan", "the widower", and "the unfed". Is this not taking the base as a foundation? How can it not be?

孤 Orphan

寡 Widower

不穀 Unfed

15

所以世上最好的称誉就是没有称誉，因为有了称誉，毁谤就随之而来了。

The best praise is no praise, because as soon as there is praise, slander also arises.

16

不要像美玉一样璀璨明亮受人重视；

Do not seek to be like jade or jewels and be paid much attention to by others;

17

而要像石头一样暗淡无光，为人忽视。

But rather be plain like stone and be passed over by others.

18

一是道所生，它也可以代表道。天地万物都由于得到了它，才能成其伟大，侯王也是由于得到了它，才能成就其高贵。但任何高贵都扎根奠基于贱下，如果没有贱下做基础，也就没有高贵了。

"The One" can be thought of as having been produced by the Dao or as another name for the Dao. All things achieve their greatness through it, and kings and princes achieve their nobility through it. But everything noble is built on a foundation of baseness. Without the base, nothing is noble.

士闻道
The Level Path

上士听见了"道"，努力不懈地去实行它；
When a superior person hears of the Dao, he puts it into practice;

1

中士听见了"道"，将信将疑；
When a mediocre person hears of the Dao, he half believes and half doubts it;

2

下士听见了"道"，哈哈大笑。
When an inferior person hears of the Dao, he laughs out loud at it;

哈！
Ha!

哈！
Ha!

哈！
Ha!

3

其实正因为下士大笑，才显得道的高深……
If he didn't laugh, it wouldn't be the Dao.

如果你这种程度的人也听得懂，那就不是道了。
If a person like you understood, there would definitely be something wrong.

4

所以古时候立言的人说过这样的话……
So it has been said in the past...

5

121

6

明道的人内含光洁，看起来好像昏暗的样子；
One who understands the Dao is bright inside but appears to be obscure;

看来一点也不起眼呀！
He's not anything worth looking at.

是啊！
I'll say.

7

进道的人，谦冲自牧，看起来好像后退的样子；
A person of the Dao is humble and self-effacing, and so appears to be retreating;

8

平坦的道，看起来好像崎岖不平的样子；
The level Dao appears rugged and uneven;

9

上德的人，谦虚卑下，好像深谷一样；
Highest virtue, being modest and lowly, is like a deep valley;

10

最洁白的好像含垢的黑色；
Greatest purity appears sullied;

11

广大的"德"，好像不足的样子；
Extensive virtue appears insufficient;

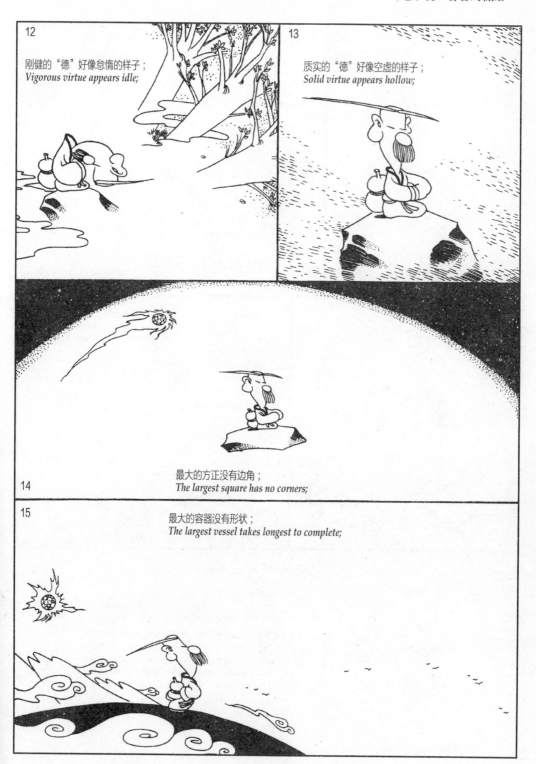

12

刚健的"德"好像怠惰的样子；
Vigorous virtue appears idle;

13

质实的"德"好像空虚的样子；
Solid virtue appears hollow;

最大的方正没有边角；
The largest square has no corners;

14

15

最大的容器没有形状；
The largest vessel takes longest to complete;

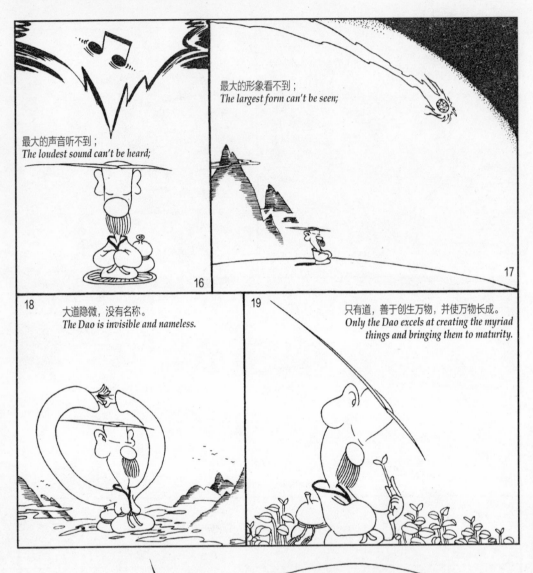

最大的声音听不到；
The loudest sound can't be heard;

最大的形象看不到；
The largest form can't be seen;

16

17

18

大道隐微，没有名称。
The Dao is invisible and nameless.

19

只有道，善于创生万物，并使万物长成。
Only the Dao excels at creating the myriad things and bringing them to maturity.

道的内在和外在完全相反，底蕴和现象完全异趣，"道德"所呈现的特质是异于常情、出乎常理的。只有上士能明了，怪不得普通人听了不易体会。
The interior and exterior of the Dao are completely opposite; its reality and manifestation are completely different. The characteristics of virtue are uncommon, and yet they spring from common sense. Since this is the case, it's no wonder that only the superior person can understand.

大成若缺
A Model for
the World

1

最完满的东西像有欠缺的样子，但是它的作用永不停止。
The most complete thing seems to be lacking, yet its usefulness is never-ending.

2

最充盈的东西好像是空虚的样子，但是它的作用永不穷竭。
The most replete thing seems to be empty, yet its usefulness is inexhaustible.

3

最正直的东西好像是弯曲的样子，
The straightest of things appears bent,

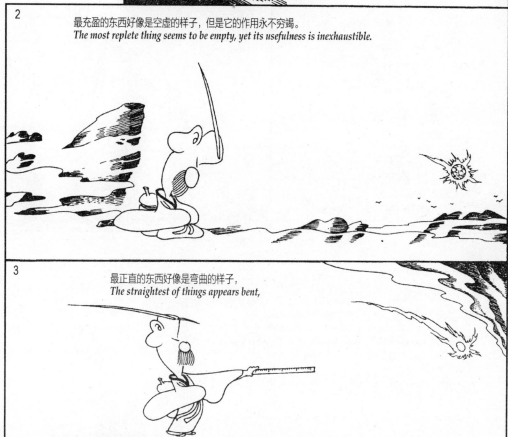

最灵巧的东西好像是笨拙的样子。
The most agile of things appears clumsy,

最卓越的辩才好像是口讷的样子。
And the greatest eloquence appears inarticulate.

4

5

6

清静克服扰动，寒冷克服暑热。
Quietude overcomes frenzy; cold overcomes heat.

静
So tranquil.

7

清静无为可以做天下人的模范。
Tranquil non-action can be a model for the world.

一个完美的人格，不在于外形上的表露，而为内在生命的含藏内敛。道体清虚寂静，但其作用却能胜躁制动，若能善体清静，无为无事，顺应自然，就可以作为天下人的表率。
A perfect character is not exhibited on the outside, but is concealed on the inside. The substance of the Dao is empty and quiet, yet the functioning of the Dao can overcome restlessness and activity. If we are good at quietude, non-action, non-interference, and following nature, then we can be models for the rest of the world.

道生之，德畜之
Profound Virtue

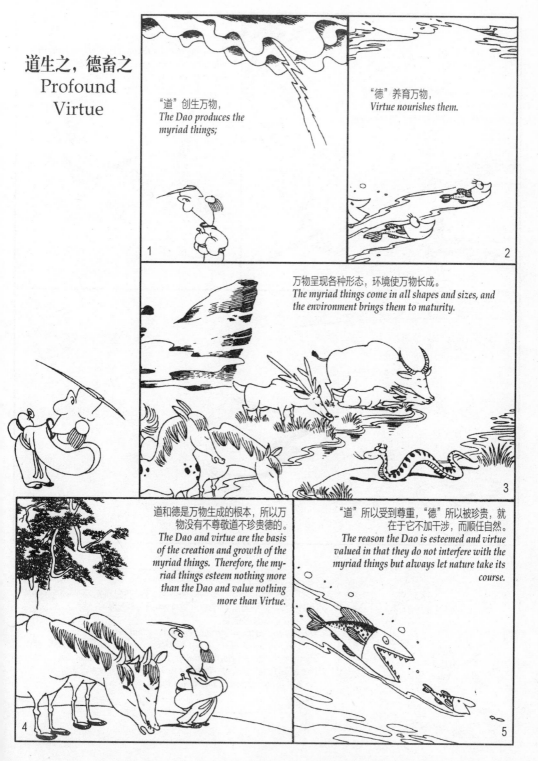

1
"道"创生万物，
The Dao produces the
myriad things;

2
"德"养育万物，
Virtue nourishes them.

3
万物呈现各种形态，环境使万物长成。
The myriad things come in all shapes and sizes, and
the environment brings them to maturity.

4
道和德是万物生成的根本，所以万
物没有不尊敬道不珍贵德的。
The Dao and virtue are the basis
of the creation and growth of the
myriad things. Therefore, the myriad things esteem nothing more
than the Dao and value nothing
more than Virtue.

5
"道"所以受到尊重，"德"所以被珍贵，就
在于它不加干涉，而顺任自然。
The reason the Dao is esteemed and virtue
valued in that they do not interfere with the
myriad things but always let nature take its
course.

所以"道"创生万物，"德"畜养万物，使万物成长作育，使万物成熟结果，使万物爱养调护。
The Dao produces them, while virtue fosters them, allows them to grow, nurtures them, brings them to maturity, and protects them.

创生万物却不据为己有，兴作万物却不自恃己能，长养万物却不为主宰。
Producing without taking as one's own, nurturing without presuming upon one's abilities, bringing to maturity without trying to control...

6

7

这就是最深的"德"。
This is the most profound virtue.

8

"道德"创造万物，都是本之于自然，它不支配万物，不干涉万物，而听任万物自然生长，这种无私无欲就是道德的伟大之处，所以能得万物的尊敬。
The Dao and virtue create the myriad things but entirely with spontaneity as the basis. They do not control or interfere with them, just allowing them to develop naturally. The greatness of the Dao and virtue lies in this lack of selfishness and desire, and it is why they are held in high regard by the myriad things.

天下有始
The Doors
of
Perception

天地万物都有个本始，作为天地万物的根源。
If there was a beginning to the world, it can be considered the mother of the world.

Dao 道

1

如果得知根源，就能认识由这母体所创生出来的子——天下万物。
If you recognize the origin, then you can come to know the children that this mother produced— the myriad things.

道 *Dao*

2

如果认识万物，又能紧守住天地万物之母的道，终身都不会有危殆。
If you can recognize the children, and if you can maintain the Dao of the mother of the myriad things, you will never come to harm.

3

堵塞情欲的孔道，关闭情欲的大门，使情欲无从产生，就终身都没有劳扰的事。
If you can close the passageways and doors of desire, not allowing desire to arise, you will be untroubled your whole life.

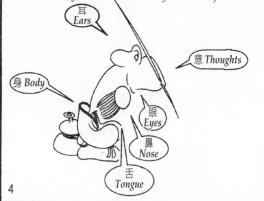

耳 *Ears*
意 *Thoughts*
身 *Body*
眼 *Eyes*
鼻 *Nose*
舌 *Tongue*

4

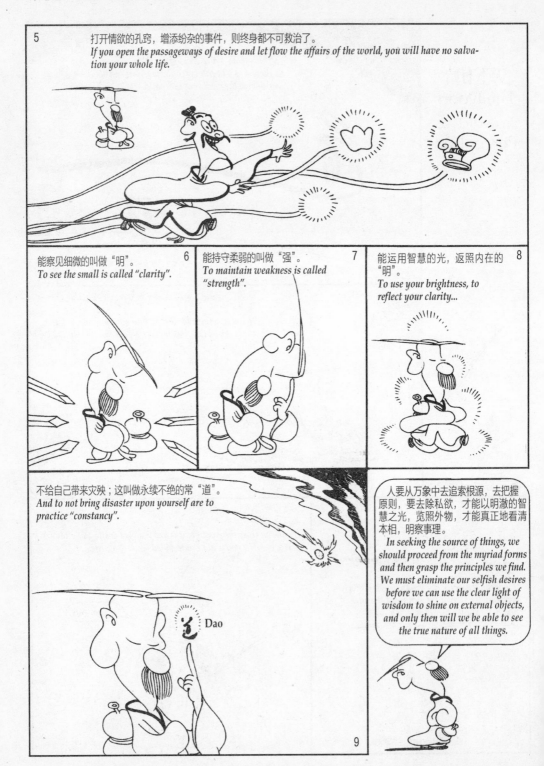

5

打开情欲的孔窍，增添纷杂的事件，则终身都不可救治了。
If you open the passageways of desire and let flow the affairs of the world, you will have no salvation your whole life.

6

能察见细微的叫做"明"。
To see the small is called "clarity".

7

能持守柔弱的叫做"强"。
To maintain weakness is called "strength".

8

能运用智慧的光，返照内在的"明"。
To use your brightness, to reflect your clarity...

不给自己带来灾殃；这叫做永续不绝的常"道"。
And to not bring disaster upon yourself are to practice "constancy".

Dao

9

人要从万象中去追索根源，去把握原则，要去除私欲，才能以明澈的智慧之光，览照外物，才能真正地看清本相，明察事理。
In seeking the source of things, we should proceed from the myriad forms and then grasp the principles we find. We must eliminate our selfish desires before we can use the clear light of wisdom to shine on external objects, and only then will we be able to see the true nature of all things.

大　道
The
Great Path

1 假使我稍微有些认识，在大道上行走，就会小心警惕，
If I were walking along a great path that I was only slightly familiar with,

2 唯恐走入了邪路。
All I would fear would be going astray.

3 大道很平坦，但是人君却喜欢走小径、行邪路。
The great Dao is level, yet people prefer the by-ways.

4 而弄得朝廷非常混乱；
The court is so very chaotic,

说！
Say it!

喝！
Take that!

5 田地非常荒芜；
The fields so very barren,

131

仓库非常的空虚。
And the granaries so very empty...

民间闹饥荒了，陛下。
Something about famine and rebellion, sire.

而他们自己却穿着锦绣的衣服，佩着锐利的刀剑……
Yet there are those who dress in silk brocade and gird themselves with sharp swords...

6

7

8

吃着丰盛的酒食，搜刮来的钱财货物怎么用也用不完。
Who drink and feast and keep vast amounts of wealth.

9

这种人简直是强盗头子，他们的行为实在不合乎于道啊！
This is banditry; it is not the Dao!

为政者，应该无私无欲，表现无为，这才合乎大道。若只为自己之利，搜刮财货，这与大盗有什么不同？
A public servant should be selfless, without desires, and should work through non-action—this is being in accord with the great Dao. If you work only for your own benefit, you might as well be plundering for spoils. What does that have to do with the Dao?

善建者不拔
Cultivating Virtue

1 善于建立的，不会被拔掉；
One who excels in establishing will not be plucked out;

道
Dao

2 善于抱持的，不会被脱去。
One who excels in embracing will not be pulled away.

德
Virtue

3 建德抱道，不仅自己可以享受福禄，并可泽及子孙，世世不辍，祭祀永享。
If you establish and embrace virtue, not only will you enjoy good fortune, but your descendants will honor you forever.

4 这个道德一定要确实身体力行才成。
This virtue must be present in all you do.

5 拿它来修身，他的德必定会充实；
If you cultivate your body with it, your virtue will be genuine;

贯彻到一家，他的德可以有余；贯彻到一乡，他的德能受到尊崇；贯彻到一国，他的德就会丰盛，贯彻到天下，他的德就会普遍。
If you cultivate your family with it, virtue will be overflowing; if you cultivate your village with it, virtue will be enduring; if you cultivate your country with it, virtue will be plentiful, and if you cultivate the world with it, virtue will be universal.

6

所以只要我修德，就能像镜子一样反照。
Therefore, if I cultivate virtue, I can emulate a mirror...

7

以我一身，观察别人；
I can use myself to view other people;

8

以我一家，观察其他各家；以我一乡，观察其他各乡；以我一国，观察其他各国；以我现在的天下，观察过去和未来的天下。
I can use my own household to view other households; I can use my own village to view other villages; I can use my own country to view other countries; And I can use the present state of the world to view the worlds of the past and the future.

9

我怎么能够知道天下的情形呢？就是由于这个道理。
How do I know this about the world? From the above reasoning.

10

"修身"犹如巩固根基，是建立身我与处人治世的基点。能以自己的善看出别人的不善。
Self-cultivation is like setting down firm roots; it is the point of departure in establishing oneself and in interacting with others.

134

含德之厚
An Infant's
Virtue

1 含"德"深厚的人，就像天真无邪的婴儿一样。
One who has an abundance of virtue is like an innocent babe.

嘻嘻! Hee hee!

2 婴儿不识不知，柔弱冲和，纯然是一团天理，所以毒虫不刺伤他，
An infant is ignorant, weak, and helpless, a little ball of pure nature, so harmful creatures don't sting it,

3 猛兽不伤害他，凶鸟不搏击他。
Vicious beasts don't maul it, and birds of prey don't seize it.

4 他筋骨柔弱，拳头却握得很牢固。
Although it's flesh and bones are soft, it's grip is firm.

他虽然不知道男女交合的事情，但小生殖器却常勃起，是因为他精气充足的缘故。
Although it doesn't yet know the union of male and female, its organ rises. This is because its essence is complete.

5

他整天号哭，可是嗓子却不会哑，这是因为他元气淳和的缘故。
It can cry and scream all day without becoming hoarse. This is because its inner harmony is complete.

哇哇!
Wah!

6

能够知道这个柔和的道理的，就能合于常道，知道这个常道的就可称为清明。
To understand this principle of gentleness is to be in accord with the constant Dao. To understand the constant Dao is to be enlightened.

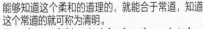

7

8

如果不知道这个常道，而纵欲享受，过分养生，就会产生灾祸。
If you don't understand the constant Dao and instead indulge your desires and nurture life too much, you will bring disaster upon yourself.

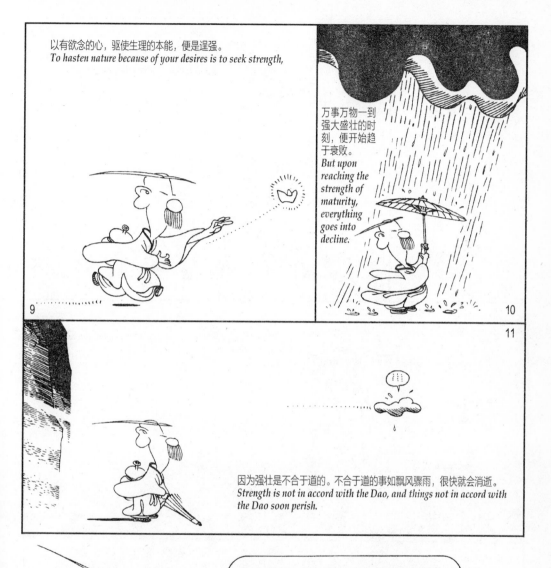

以有欲念的心，驱使生理的本能，便是逞强。
To hasten nature because of your desires is to seek strength,

万事万物一到强大盛壮的时刻，便开始趋于衰败。
But upon reaching the strength of maturity, everything goes into decline.

9

10

11

因为强壮是不合于道的。不合于道的事如飘风骤雨，很快就会消逝。
Strength is not in accord with the Dao, and things not in accord with the Dao soon perish.

人初生的时候，无知无欲可以说是德性最厚的时候，等到长大以后，嗜欲日深，诈伪日增，便渐渐失道失德了。得道的人就像婴儿一样柔弱、纯洁、无知无欲，但却充满生机，处处顺应自然，自在自得。
When people are just born, they are without knowledge or desire. You could say that this is when their virtue is most abundant. When they have grown up, their interests and desires increase daily, as does their hypocrisy, and gradually they lose the Dao and Virtue.
A person who has attained the Dao is as soft and weak, pure and innocent as and infant, yet he is full of vitality and natural and carefree in every way.

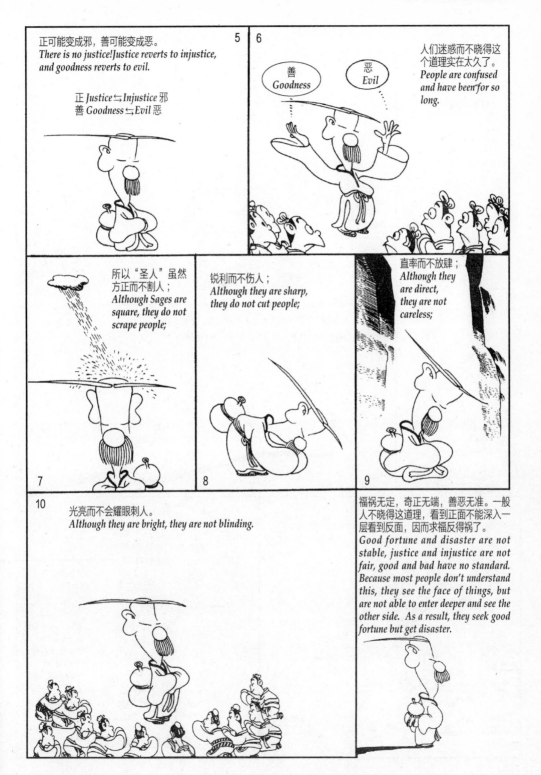

5
正可能变成邪，善可能变成恶。
There is no justice! Justice reverts to injustice, and goodness reverts to evil.

正 *Justice* ⇆ *Injustice* 邪
善 *Goodness* ⇆ *Evil* 恶

6
善
Goodness

恶
Evil

人们迷惑而不晓得这个道理实在太久了。
People are confused and have been for so long.

7
所以"圣人"虽然方正而不割人；
Although Sages are square, they do not scrape people;

8
锐利而不伤人；
Although they are sharp, they do not cut people;

9
直率而不放肆；
Although they are direct, they are not careless;

10
光亮而不会耀眼刺人。
Although they are bright, they are not blinding.

福祸无定，奇正无端，善恶无准。一般人不晓得这道理，看到正面不能深入一层看到反面，因而求福反得祸了。
Good fortune and disaster are not stable, justice and injustice are not fair, good and bad have no standard. Because most people don't understand this, they see the face of things, but are not able to enter deeper and see the other side. As a result, they seek good fortune but get disaster.

俭嗇
Frugality

治理国家，养护身心，最好的方法莫过于爱惜精神。
In governing people and nurturing life, nothing is better than frugality.

1

因为只有爱惜精神，才能在灾祸来临之前，及早服从于道；
Only in frugality can you get right to following the Dao.

2

Dao
道

及早服从于道，就是厚积德；
Getting right to following the Dao is to accumulate much virtue.

德
Virtue

3

无为，又无所不为……
I do nothing, and nothing is left undone...

能够厚积德，做到清静、无为、自然，就没有事不能克服；
With an accumulation of much virtue, so that you are tranquil, non-active, and natural, there will be nothing that you cannot overcome;

4

5

事事都能克服，没有什么不能胜任，就无法估计他的力量；
When there is nothing that you cannot overcome, your power will be beyond measure;

6

无法估计他的力量，就可以担负保护国家的责任；
When your power is beyond measure, you can take up the responsibilities of protecting a country;

Governing through non-action

掌握治理国家的道理，就可以维持长久，这就是根深蒂固、长久存在的道理。
And when you take up the responsibilities of protecting a country in this way, you can endure. This is called "establishing deep roots and solid stalks", and it is the principle of "an enduring life and lasting vision".

7

俭啬，才能修养天机，蓄积精神，培蓄能量、充实内在生命，而达到纯真质朴的境界。
Only through frugality can you cultivate your natural potential, accumulate energy, bring out ability, and preserve your life within, while also achieving a realm of purity and simplicity.

141

大者宜为下
The Lowly Superpower

大国要像江海一样，居于下流，为天下所归汇。
A large country is like a body of water in that it abides in lowliness—it is the confluence of all the world.

1

自居于下天雌柔的位置，雌柔常常以静定而胜于雄强，因为静定而又能处下的缘故。
It resides in all that is feminine in the world. The female uses quietude to win over the male and it is in this quietude that she is lowly.

2

所以大国对小国谦下，就可以会聚小国；小国对大国谦下，就可以见容于大国。
A large country takes a position below smaller countries and thereby gains the allegiance of smaller countries. A small country takes a position below larger countries, and thereby is taken in by larger countries.

3

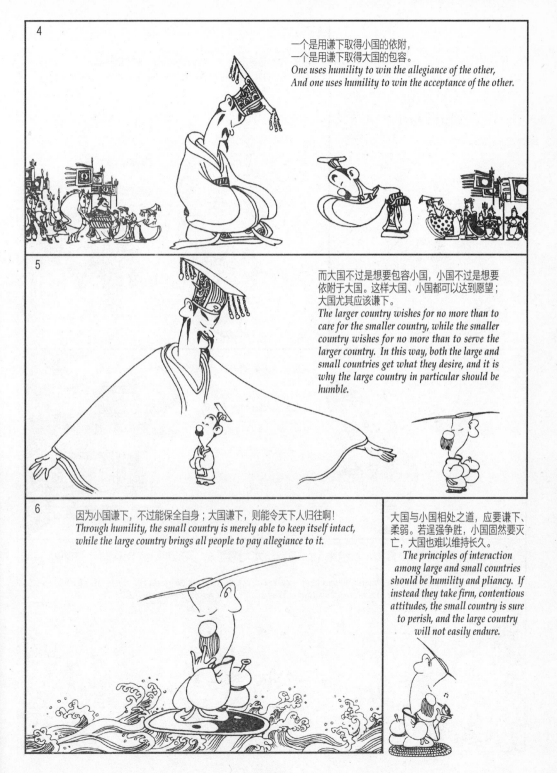

4

一个是用谦下取得小国的依附，
一个是用谦下取得大国的包容。
One uses humility to win the allegiance of the other,
And one uses humility to win the acceptance of the other.

5

而大国不过是想要包容小国，小国不过是想要依附于大国。这样大国、小国都可以达到愿望；大国尤其应该谦下。
The larger country wishes for no more than to care for the smaller country, while the smaller country wishes for no more than to serve the larger country. In this way, both the large and small countries get what they desire, and it is why the large country in particular should be humble.

6

因为小国谦下，不过能保全自身；大国谦下，则能令天下人归往啊！
Through humility, the small country is merely able to keep itself intact, while the large country brings all people to pay allegiance to it.

大国与小国相处之道，应要谦下、柔弱。若逞强争胜，小国固然要灭亡，大国也难以维持长久。
The principles of interaction among large and small countries should be humility and pliancy. If instead they take firm, contentious attitudes, the small country is sure to perish, and the large country will not easily endure.

道者万物之奥
Prizing
the Dao

1

道是万物中最尊贵的。善人用道立身行事，把道看作宝贝；
The Dao is the treasury of the myriad things, and the treasure of the good person;

道
Dao

2

生命的法……
The principle of life...

道
Dao

不善的人也不敢违背道，而时时保守着它。
A bad person also seeks to protect it rather than defy it.

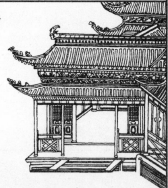

3

善人修道，说出话来都美好感人，能得到别人的尊敬；做出事来都美好感人，可以用来作为别人的法则。不善的人，怎能把道舍弃呢？
A person who cultivates the Dao is an impressive speaker and can thereby win the respect of others. He also performs impressive deeds and so is accepted by others. Why would a bad person forsake the Dao?

道
Dao

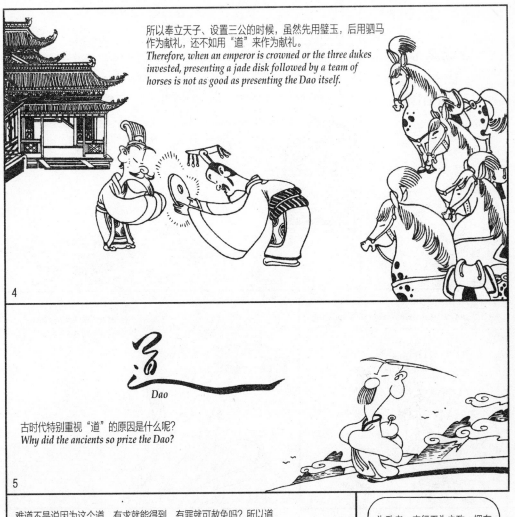

所以奉立天子、设置三公的时候，虽然先用璧玉，后用驷马作为献礼，还不如用"道"来作为献礼。

Therefore, when an emperor is crowned or the three dukes invested, presenting a jade disk followed by a team of horses is not as good as presenting the Dao itself.

4

Dao

古时代特别重视"道"的原因是什么呢？
Why did the ancients so prize the Dao?

5

难道不是说因为这个道，有求就能得到，有罪就可赦免吗？所以道实在是天下最贵重的了。
Isn't it said: "With it one attains what one seeks. With it, one's transgressions are pardoned?"
For this reason, it is the prize of all the land.

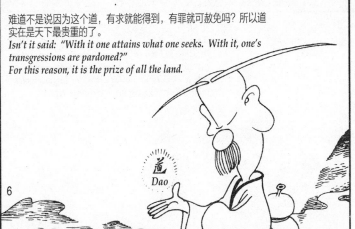

Dao

6

为政者，应行无为之政，拥有拱璧驷马，不如怀着清静无为的心念，循道而行。
For a ruler to have a mind of tranquillity and non-action that allows him to follow the Dao is much more important than having a jade disk and a team of horses.

多易必多难
Easing
Difficulties

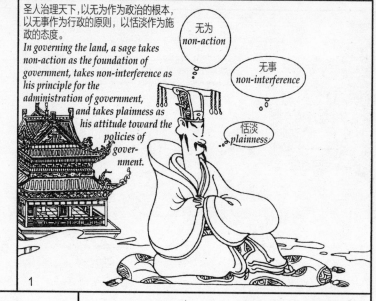

圣人治理天下，以无为作为政治的根本，以无事作为行政的原则，以恬淡作为施政的态度。

In governing the land, a sage takes non-action as the foundation of government, takes non-interference as his principle for the administration of government, and takes plainness as his attitude toward the policies of government.

无为
non-action

无事
non-interference

恬淡
plainness

1

处理困难必从容易处开始；
A difficulty is overcome through its simplicity;

2

实现远大目标必从细微处开始。
A great task is accomplished through its insignificance.

3

天下的难事，必定从容易的做起；天下的大事，必定从细微的做起。

In other words, in approaching the most difficult affairs in the land, one must begin from the simple aspects; and in handling the largest issues in the land, one must begin with the details.

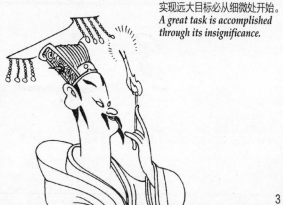

易
Easy

难
Difficult

4

所以圣人始终不自以为伟大，因而反能成就他的伟大。
The sage never sets out to accomplish great things, and this is how he is able to achieve greatness.

5

再困难的事，交给我必定从容完成。
No problem. Of course I'll do it.

轻易的允诺，必常因不能兑现而失信；
Blithe promises are seldom fulfilled;

6

把事情看得太容易，必经常遭遇困难。
And the easier one takes something to be, the more difficult it will be.

轻 *Light*　重 *Heavy*

7

圣人把任何事都看得很困难，所以始终不会发生什么困难。
So, a sage sees everything as difficult, and for this reason, he has no difficulties.

难 *difficult*

易 *easy*

8

处理艰难的事情，须先从细易处着手。面临细易的事情，却不可轻心，应谨密周思、细心而为才不会失败。
When dealing with a difficulty, start from the minor and easy aspects of it, but when you do, don't take them lightly. Only by being thorough and careful can you keep from failing.

慎终如始
Planning
and
Perseverance

安定的局面，容易持守；没有迹象的事情，容易图谋。
A stable situation is easy to maintain, and a situation that has yet to reveal omens is easy to plan for.

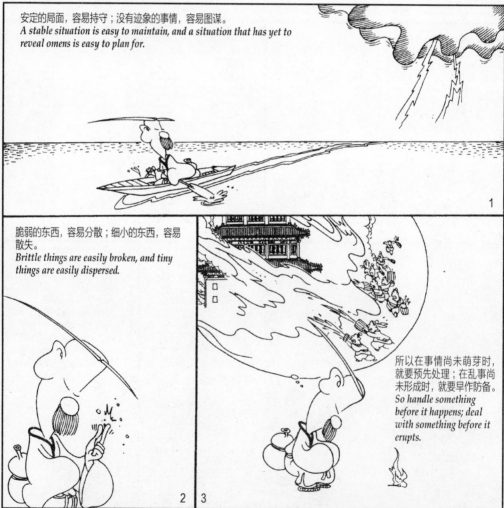

1

脆弱的东西，容易分散；细小的东西，容易散失。
Brittle things are easily broken, and tiny things are easily dispersed.

所以在事情尚未萌芽时，就要预先处理；在乱事尚未形成时，就要早作防备。
So handle something before it happens; deal with something before it erupts.

2 3

合抱的大木，是从嫩芽长起来的；
A tree that you can barely embrace began from a tiny sprout;

九层的高台，是由一筐筐泥土筑起来的；
A nine story tower began as a pile of dirt;

千里的远行，是由一步步走出来的。
A thousand mile journey begins with a single step.

人们做事情，常常在快要成功时候遭受失败。若在事情要完成时也能像开始时一样的谨慎，那就不会败事了。
When people do things, they often go part way then fail. But if you can be as careful at the end as you are at the beginning, you will never fail.

平常心
The ordinary mind

凡事从小到大，由近至远，远大的事情必须有毅力和耐心一点一滴去完成；心稍松懈，常会功亏一篑。
In whatever you do, proceed from the small to the large, from the near to the distant.

In large and laborious tasks, you must work with persistence and patience. If you slack off just a bit, you are likely to fall just that much short of your goal.

以愚治国
Mysterious
Virtue

1

古时代善于用道治国的人，不是要人民明智机巧，而是要人民质朴敦厚。

The ancients who excelled at employing the Dao in governing, did not strive to make the people intelligent and cunning, but to make them simple and generous.

2

用什么办法对付人民……

How am I going to keep them in line...

人民所以难治，是因为他们智巧诡诈太多的原故。

The reason people became difficult to govern is that they became too intelligent and cunning.

想办法对付政府……

We gotta fight the government...

3

所以用智巧去治理国家，是国家的灾祸，不用智巧去治理国家，是国家的幸福。

So governing through cunning means will ensure disaster. Not governing through cunning means is the good fortune of a country.

了解这两种治国方式的差别，而有所取舍，就是一种法则。长久地记住并实行这一法则，可以称为玄妙无上的德。
The difference between these two ways of governing is an important principle to be maintained. Understanding and practicing this principle is called "mysterious virtue".

4

这玄妙无上的德既深奥，又久远，它和万事万物相反，可是依循它而行，却可顺合于自然。
This mysterious virtue is profound and far-reaching! It returns with all things, and by following it, you will join the great flow of nature.

5

世乱的根源莫过于大家攻心斗智，竞相伪饰，于是就弄得国无宁日了。人人扬弃世俗价值的争纷而返归真朴，社会才能趋于安宁。
Nothing ensures a chaotic world like aggressiveness and contention. If everyone were to abandon the petty contentions brought on by conventional values and return to simplicity, society would tend toward tranquillity.

三宝
The Three Treasures

我有三样宝贝，持守而保全着。第一样叫做慈爱；第二样叫做俭啬；第三样叫做不敢居于天下人之先。

I have three treasures. I keep and protect them. The first is called "compassion"; The second is called "frugality"; The third is called "an unwillingness to be first".

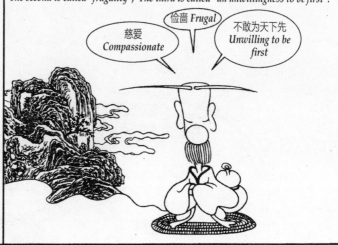

慈爱
Compassionate

俭啬 Frugal

不敢为天下先
Unwilling to be first

1

慈爱，就能维护众生，所以产生勇气；

With compassion, one can protect other creatures, and this produces courage.

哇!
Waa!

2

俭啬，就能蓄精积德，所以能推致广远；

With frugality, one can nurture the spirit and store up virtue, and these can be extended far and wide.

爱惜精神
Nurture the spirit.

积存智识
Store up virtue.

3

不敢居于天下人之先，则反而得到爱戴，所以能成为万物的首长。

With an unwillingness to be first, one gains the respect of others and can therefore act as leader.

谦下和退让
Humble and yielding.

他很客气，其实他很棒！
He's just being modest. He's actually very capable!

4

如果不能慈爱而只求勇敢……
Courage without compassion...

不能俭啬而只求广远……
Broad expression without frugality...

不能居人之后而只求争先，那必是死路一条了。
And leading without humility ensure certain doom!

当仁不让!
In being benevolent, one should not yield!

5　**6**　**7**

三宝之中，慈爱最重要，用慈爱的心对待矛盾，则能获胜；用慈爱的心防守，则能巩固。
Of the three treasures, compassion is the most important. If you employ compassion in battle, you will win; if you employ it in defense, you will be well-grounded.

8

能够发挥慈爱的人，天也要救助他，卫护他。
When Heaven goes to save someone, It protects him out of compassion.

爱心加上同情心是人类友好相处的基本动力，人人若能有天地对万物一律平等的大爱，世上将不再有纷争。
Love with compassion is the fundamental motivation for friendly intercourse. If people can emulate nature's loving fairness toward all things, there will be no more contentions in the world.

9

153

用兵
Warfare

古代用兵的人曾这样说过：
There is a saying for warfare:

我不敢主动挑起战端，而采取守势；我不敢逞强争胜前进一寸，而宁可退后一尺。
I dare not be the first to attack, and instead set up a defense; I dare not advance an inch, and instead retreat a foot.

1

这就是说：虽然有阵势，却像没有阵势可摆；
This is to say that although you are in formation, you should give the appearance that you are not;

2

虽然要奋臂，却像没臂膀可举；
When you want to take up arms, make it appear that you have none;

3

虽然面临敌人，却像没有敌人可赴；
Although you are facing your enemy, give the appearance that you have no enemies;

你好，朋友！
Hello, friend!

4

虽然有兵器，但持用时像没有兵器可持。
Although you have weapons, give the appearance that you do not;

所以时时都要怀着一颗哀慈不争的心。
Always maintain a compassionate and non-contentious attitude.

5

6

军队的祸患没有比逞强无敌更大的了。
There is no greater disaster than underestimating an enemy.

逞强无敌会丧失我的三宝。
If we underestimate the enemy, we could lose our three treasures.

呼!
Boom!

7

8

9

举兵相交战的时候，有慈爱之心的一方会获得胜利。
When two forces battle, the compassionate one will be victorious.

战争是万不得已的，若不幸非面临战争不可时，应不挑衅、不侵略、不轻敌。不轻易使用武力制敌。
War should only occur as a last resort. When it must be faced, do not provoke, do not invade, and do not underestimate the enemy. And do not blithely go into battle.

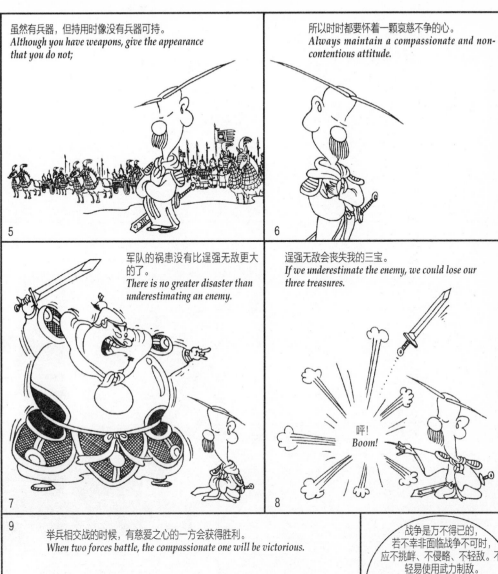

圣人怀玉
Heart of Jade

我的言论很容易了解，也很容易实行。
My words are very easy to understand, and very easy to practice.

但是天下人都被私欲所蒙蔽，都被名利所迷惑，而没有人能够了解，没有人能够实行。
But because everyone is blinded by selfish desires and confused by fame and wealth, no one is able to understand or practice them.

利 Profit

财 Wealth

私欲 desires

名 Fame

我的言论都有本源，我的行事都有根据。
There is a source for my words; there is a basis for my actions.

正因为人们不懂我的言论和行事，所以也就不了解我了。
It is because people understand neither my words nor my actions that they don't understand me.

了解我的人很少，取法跟随我的就更难得了。
Those who understand me are few, and those who emulate me are even harder to come by.

因为，圣人外面穿着粗衣，内里却怀着美玉。
This is why sages wear coarse cloth while harboring a heart of jade.

虚静、柔和、慈俭、不争，这都本于自然的道理，在日常生活上最容易实行，可惜世人只慕恋虚华的外表，看不到圣人身怀的美玉。
Emptiness, quietude, pliancy, harmony, compassion, frugality, and non-contentiousness are natural principles and are the easiest things to practice. Unfortunately, most people adore only splendid exteriors and cannot see the sage's heart of jade.

民不畏威
Tyranny

1 当人民不再畏惧统治者的苛政暴刑威压时……
When the people no longer fear a tyrant's oppression...

2 那么更大的祸乱就要发生了。
An even greater calamity is immanent.

所以治国者不要协迫人民的生存，
Therefore, do not exploit the people's livelihood,

不要压榨人民的生活。
Do not oppress the people's lives.

没有米了！
We have no rice left!

拿来！
Hand it over!

3

4

正因为统治者不压榨人民，不胁迫人民，人民才不厌弃他而推戴他。
Because the sage neither exploits nor oppresses the people, they do not turn on him, but rather turn toward him.

5

所以圣人了解自己位居万民之上，不求自我表现；但求自爱而不自显高贵。
The sage understands himself but does not display himself. He cares about himself but does not glorify himself.

6

所以舍弃自见、自贵，而取其自知、自爱。
Therefore, discard all thought of displaying and glorifying yourself, and simply understand and care for yourself.

7

暴政逼迫、压制人民的自由、生活，人民到了无法安居、无以安生时就会铤而走险、革命造反了。
When a tyrannical government oppresses the people's freedom and livelihood so that the people can no longer live comfortably and in peace, they will risk everything and revolt.

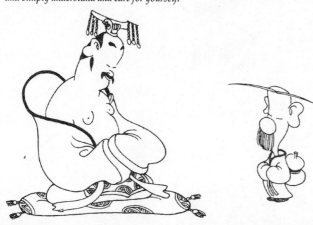

代大匠斲
Standing
In for
the Carpenter

1

人民饱受苛刑暴政的逼迫，到了不怕一死而起来反抗时，执政者怎么能用死来威胁他们呢？

When the people are fed up with the tyranny of government to the point that they will risk death in revolt, how can a government continue to use death as a threat?

如果人民真的畏惧死亡，
If the people do fear death however,

2

天地间冥冥之中，一直有专司杀生者来主持生死，不需要人来代劳。
Nature has always been the arbiter of life and death. It does not need a tyrant to stand in for it.

3

一有做坏事的人，我就抓来杀掉，谁还敢胡作非为呢？
And we execute the first criminal that comes along, then who would dare turn to crime?

Ahh!

4

5

如果要代替天地之间的杀生者来主持杀戮，
Someone standing in as arbiter of death,

替天行道。
I carry out the will of Heaven.

我来代你砍。
Let me do it.

这就好像一个不会工艺的人代替木匠去砍断木头一样。
Is like standing in for a carpenter who is splitting wood.

6

7

代替木匠砍断木头，很少有不砍伤自己的手的。
It is not often that the one who stands in does not injure his own hand.

哇!
Ahh!

自然界的生死自有其规律，不需要治政者用严刑暴政去代天杀人，替天杀戮者，自己也将受到伤害。
Life and death follow a natural order. Nature does not need an arbitrary tyrant to stand in for it, and anyone who does is likely to end up harmed himself.

民之饥
Starvation
and
Taxes

人民之所以饥饿，是因为税赋太多，因此陷于饥饿。
People go hungry because food taxes are too high.

再征收去，我们都得饿死！
If you take anymore we'll starve to death!

1

人民之所以难治，是因为统治者强作妄为，因此难以管治。
People are difficult to govern because rulers often do too much.

政令朝令夕改，叫我们如何遵循？
They issue one order in the morning, then change it in the evening. How are we supposed to keep up?

2

人民之所以轻死，是因为统治者奉养奢厚，因此轻于犯死。　**3**
People take death lightly because their rulers pursue lavish lives.

活着也无以维生，不如跟他拼了！
We can't make a living anyway, so we'd rather take them down with us!

因此统治者恬淡无欲，清静无为，比起贵生奉养要来得高明多了。　**4**
Thus, a more enlightened ruler will govern quietly and without desires, rather than pursue too much.

剥削与高压是政治祸乱的，根本，在上者横征暴敛，人民自然会从饥饿死亡的边缘中挺身抗争。
Exploitation and oppression are the roots of political chaos. When rulers are tyrannical, the people will rise up from the edge of starvation and death to fight back.

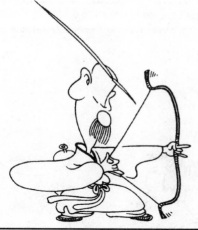

天道犹张弓
The Drawn Bow

自然的规律，岂不就像拉弓一样吗？
Isn't the law of nature like a drawn bow?

弦位高了，就把它压低；
If the bow is too high, you lower it;

1

2

弦位低了，就把它升高；
If it is too low, you raise it;

弦长了就把它缩短，弦短了就把它加长。
If the string is too long, you shorten it;If it is too short, you lengthen it.

3

4

自然的规律是减少有余，用来补充不足。
The law of nature reduces surplus and supplements any insufficiency in the world.

5

但社会的法规却不是这样，而是剥夺不足用来供奉有余。
Unlike the laws of society, which reduce insufficiency and supplement surplus.

哇！劫贫济富。
He's taking from the poor to give to the rich!

给你。
This is for you.

谢谢。
Thank you.

6

谁能够把有余的拿来供给天下不足的？
Who can take a surplus and supplement the insufficiencies of the world?

7

这只有有道的人才能做到。
Only a person of the Dao.

8

自然的规律是拿有余来补不足，而保持均平调和的原则。社会的规则应效法自然的规律的均平调和，才能使社会达到完满和谐。
The laws of nature redistribute things in order to maintain an equilibrium. Only by emulating nature and seeking this kind of equilibrium can society achieve harmony.

小国寡民
The Ideal Country

理想的国家是：国土很小，人民很少。
The ideal country is as follows: A small area of land and a small number of people.

买一斤橘子。
I'll have a pound of tangerines, please.

1

没有冲突纷争，纵使拥有各种兵器也不运用。
There are no conflicts, so even though there are all kinds of weapons, they go unused.

2

没有苛刑暴政，人民不需要冒着生命的危险迁移到远方。
The government is not tyrannical, so the people needn't move far away.

3

虽有船只车辆，也没有机会去乘坐。
There are boats and carts, but no one needs to use them.

4

虽有铠甲武器，也没有机会去展示。
Although there are armor and weapons, there is no need to display them.

白当了五十年军人，没机会表现，派不上用场。
I've wasted fifty years as a soldier. I've never even gotten to go to battle.

5

使人民回复到古代用结绳来记事。
The people return to the old ways and use knots to record things.

6

人民恬淡寡欲，吃的虽是粗食，但觉得很甘美；
People are simple and without desires, so although everyone eats plain food, it tastes delicious;

7

穿的虽是破衣，但觉得很漂亮；
Although they wear coarse clothing, it looks beautiful;

8

住的虽是陋室，但觉得很安适；
Although they live in humble dwellings, they are comfortable;

9

风俗虽很简朴，但觉得很快乐。
And although the customs are simple, the people are very happy.

10

和邻国之间彼此都看得到，鸡鸣狗叫的声音也彼此听得到……
They see the people of neighboring countries and can even hear their chickens and dogs......

11

12 由于民风是如此纯厚质朴，大家都没有什么需求，所以人民从生到死，也不相往来。整个天下一片淳朴。
but because the people lead simple lives and have few needs, they live to an old age without ever going to visit other countries.

小国寡民，社会秩序无须镇制力量来维持，单凭纯良的本能就可相安无事。因为没有战争祸乱、没有暴戾风气，民风淳朴真实，人们没有焦虑不安的情绪，没有恐惧失落的感受，故能安和乐利恬淡无欲。
In a small country with a small population, social order can be maintained without suppression, depending instead on the goodness of the simple populace. Because there are no catastrophes resulting from war nor an atmosphere of violence, the people are honest and trustworthy. Because the people have no worries of instability and no fear of loss, they can live in simplicity, peace, and happiness.

诸子谈黄老经

Ancient Thinkers
Discuss the Dao

道可道，非常道。
*If the Dao can be
explained, it is not
the constant Dao.*

——《道德经》第一章
—*Dao De Jing,
Chap.1*

名可名，非常名。

If a name can be named, it is not a constant name.

——《道德经》第一章
—Dao De Jing, Chap.1

1

无尽藏尼对六祖慧能说…
A Buddhist nun named Wujin-cang said to the sixth Zen patriarch, Hui Neng:

请替我解释这《涅槃经》吧。
I'd like you to explain a passage in the Nirvana Sutra for me.

2

对不起，我不认识字，请你把经文念出来，我可以略解其中的真理。
I'm sorry, but I can't read. You go ahead and read it to me, and then I'll explain it.

3

连字都不认得，怎能了解其中的真理?
If you can't even read the words, how can you understand the principles behind them?

4

真理是和文字无关的。文字像您我的手指。
The truth is independent of language. Language is like my finger.

5

手指可以指出明月的所在，但手指却不是明月，看月也不一定要透过手指啊。
I can point out the moon with it, but it is not the moon. And you don't need to point at the moon to see it.

文字像是手指，手指指出真理，但一般人只顾看着手指，并没有往手指指的方向深入看见其中的真理……
——译自《六祖坛经》
Language is like a finger that points out the truth, but most people see only the finger, instead of looking deep into the direction the finger is pointing...

太上，不知有之。

As for the greatest kind of ruler, you don't even know he's there.

——《道德经》第十七章
--Dao De Jing, Chap. 17

1

如果一个人敏捷有力、疏通明达，这人算是好的君王吗？
What would you think of an intelligent, capable ruler-a real go-getter who gets things done?

杨朱去见老子。
Yang Zhu went to see Laozi.

2

这种人有了才能，便供人使唤，有了技艺，便被技艺系累，徒然劳动自己的形体，离开"道"是越来越远了。
When this kind of person has a certain talent, he ends up an errand-boy for others. When this kind of person achieves a certain skill, he ends up shackled by that skill. He taxes his body in vain and strays farther and farther from the Dao.

3

虎豹因为身上有文彩，被人捉去；猿猴也因为身子矫捷，被人捉去。你说它们是真正有智慧吗？
The tiger and leopard are captured for their colorful hides. Monkeys are captured because they are agile and entertaining. So, would you say they are wise?

4

好的君王究竟是如何的？
Then what does make for a good ruler?

明王治天下，不自以为有功，泽及万物，百姓不觉，这样神化莫测，才能算是好的君王啊！
In governing the land, the good ruler doesn't purposely aim at making great contributions to society, and yet his accomplishments reach everyone without anyone realizing it. Only a ruler capable of this kind of unfathomable transformation can be considered a good ruler.

最好的世代，人民根本不感到统治者的存在，没有政权的压力，大家呼吸在安闲自适的空气中。
During the best of times, people don't even notice the existence of the rulers. With no pressure from above, everyone is able to breathe free and easy in the open air.

人法地，地法天，
天法道，道法自然。

People follow the earth, the
earth follows heaven, heaven
follows the Dao,
the Dao follows nature.

——《道德经》第二十五章
–Dao De Jing, Chap. 25

1

士城绮去见
老子。
Shi Chengqi
went to see
Laozi:

听说你是有大智慧的圣人，
所以不辞千里来见你。
I've heard that you are a
wise sage
and so have
traveled
hundreds of miles
to see you.

2

但是见了你以后，真使
我大失所望！
But now that I've seen you,
I'm terribly
disappointed!

士成绮回去之后，原以为有胜利的
优越感，但心中反而一片空虚。
Shi Chengqi thought he would
have a great feeling of superiority
after his prank, but
instead, he felt
completely
empty inside.

3

我昨天骂你一顿，自以为胜利
了，但心情却很空虚，请问这
是什么缘故？
Yesterday, I felt that I had beaten
you, but then my
heart was so empty.
Why is this?

你昨日来的时候，神态高傲，像要
和人打架一样。
When you came yesterday, you were
arrogant, as
though ready to pick
a fight with someone.

4

就像边境上的野马，突然被人捉到，
便心气浮动，完全失去了它的本性。
You were like a wild horse in the hin-
terlands that is suddenly captured, and
it's heart jumps as it loses its original
nature.

5

是！是是！应该怎
么办？
Yes! Yes! What
can I do about it?

6

失去本性的人就叫做自然的贼。
你如果要修道的话，就请回复自然的本性吧！
One who has lost his original nature has robbed
nature. If you want to cultivate yourself in the Dao,
you must return to your original nature.

7

"道" 以自然为归，
"道" 的本性就是自然。
The Dao follows na-
ture; its original nature
is nature.

tag

上德不德，是以有
德；下德不失德，
是以无德。

*People of superior virtue
are not so intentionally
and are therefore vir-
tuous. People of inferior
virtue are intentionally
virtuous and are thus
not virtuous.*

——《道德经》第三十八
–Dao De Jing, chap. 38

1
梁武帝是个非常喜欢佛法的皇帝，平时经常着佛衣、吃斋念佛。

*Emperor Wu of the
Liang dynasty
(502–566) was a
devout Buddhist.
He wore Buddhist
clothes, was a
vegetarian, and
recited the
scriptures.*

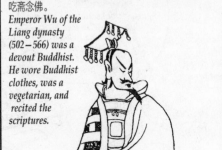

2
梁普通八年十月一日达摩祖师会见梁武帝。

*One day, the great Indian
missionary of Zen
Buddhism,
Bodhidharma, had
an audience with
the emperor.*

3
我自从即位以来，供养佛僧、建造寺庙、抄写佛经、雕塑佛像，这究竟有多大功德呢？

*Ever since I ascended the throne, I have provided for monks and nuns,
I have had temples built, had the Buddhist scriptures
copied, had statues made... How many merits will I
receive for all that I have done?*

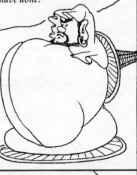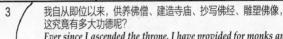

4
根本没有功德可言。
None to speak of.

5
怎么会没有
功德？
*What?! No
merits?!*

6
这些都是六道之中的小成果，一切都是迷惑的再生产，恰如影子跟随人，即使有善意也不是真实的。

*Yours are but minor earthly achievements. Your actions
were confused imitations and no more voluntary than a
shadow following a form. Even if your intentions were
good, they weren't real.*

施善事，心中不可先存
有积善德之心，如果施善事
是为了积德，便没有德了。
*When performing good
deeds, if you are doing so
just to accumulate merits
or accolades, then there is
no virtue at all in what you
are doing!*

**祸莫大于不知足，
咎莫大于欲得。**

*There is no greater disaster
than discontentment.
There is no greater crime
than greed.*

——《道德经》第四十六章
–Dao De Jing, Chap. 46

1

我想到天下各地去游历！
*I'm going to go out and
travel the land to gain
worldly experience.*

你想先到哪里？
*And where will you
go first?*

柏矩追随老聃学道。
*Bo Ju was a fol-
lower of Laozi.*

2

我先去齐国看看吧！
*I'm going to
the state of Qi
first. Bye.*

3

柏矩一踏入齐国的边界，便看到尸体。
*As soon as Bo Ju crossed the border
into Qi, the first things he
saw were dead
bodies.*

4

哎呀，真可怜啊！
*Oh no, you poor
man!*

天下最大的灾害，你就先遇上了！
*You've just come upon
the greatest disaster of
all!*

5

国法上说："不要做强盗，不要杀人！"
但是谁在做强盗？谁在杀人？
*The law says, "Don't steal and don't
kill," but who is it that is doing all of
the stealing and killing?*

6

统治者多欲生事为害，侵人国土，伤人性命，带来无穷的灾难。
*Rulers create disasters by gi-
ving free reign to their desires,
which leads them to invade
other countries, causing death
and destruction on all sides.*

175

知者不言，言者不知。
One who knows does not speak,
One who speaks does
not know.

——《道德经》第五十六章
–Dao De Jing, Chap. 56

伯昏瞀人去看列子。
One day, Bohun Wuren went to see the philosopher Liezi.

1

只见列子的门外鞋子都排满了。
But as soon as he saw all the shoes outside of Liezi's house...

2

大师! 有人找您!
Master, there's someone here to see you!

3

老师! 老师既然来了，为何不进来指教弟子呢?
Master, you've come all this way, why don't you come in and teach me.

4

理想的人格是挫锐、解纷、和光、同尘，含敛光耀。列子却偏偏光芒外露，引来很多人，这是小聪明而不是大智慧。

Ideally, a person should dull one's sharpness, disentangle one's complications, cover one's brightness, and merge with the dusty world, but Liezi just had to go and reveal his brightness, thus attracting all those people. This is an example of petty intelligence rather than great wisdom.

算了! 我早就告诉你要葆光，不要显露了形迹!
Forget it! I told you before to keep the light within yourself and not to let others see it!

现在你让人来归附你，却不能使人不归附你，这便是你露出了与众不同的痕迹啊!
You're gathering followers instead of keeping them away. You're revealing traces of uniqueness!

5

天下多忌讳，而民弥贫；
朝多利器，国家滋昏；
人多伎巧，奇物滋起。

The more prohibitions there are, the poorer the people will be. The more weapons there are, the more discordant it will be. The more cunning people are, the more wickedness there will be.

——《道德经》第五十七章
–Dao De Jing, Chap. 57

射鸟的弓箭花样越多，天空的鸟只好乱飞了。
As arrows are shot into the air, birds can only scatter in confusion.

1

捕兽的陷阱花样越多，森林里的野兽就只好乱跑了。
As a net drops into the water, fish can only swim away in confusion.

捕鱼的罗网钩子花样多了，水里的鱼只有乱窜了。
As the varieties of traps increase, animals can only flee in confusion.

2

3

人的智巧越多，欺诈、狡猾、诡辩种种花样就来了。
As people's cunning increases, the more lying, cheating, and conniving there is.

4

人类好用智巧，于是天下就大乱了！
The more people enjoy using this cunning, the more confusion there will be in the world!

5

天下的禁忌越多，人民越陷于贫困；政府的权谋越多，国家越陷于昏乱；统治者的技巧越多，邪恶的事就连连发生了。
Laws and force are a means of controlling people, a means of coercing people into submission, but the more you tell people not to do something, the more they will want to do it, and when it finally happens, the more of an uproar it will cause.

善为士者，不武；
善战者，不怒；
善胜敌者，不与。

A good general is not excessively violent, A good soldier is not easily angered, A good conqueror does not resort to confrontation.

——《道德经》第六十八章
–Dao De Jing, Chap. 68

纪渻子替周宣王养斗鸡。
A man named Ji Shengzi raised a fighting cock for the king.

斗鸡养好了没有？可以打架了吗？
Well, is he ready for a match yet?

还不能。这鸡意气很盛，斗志高昂。
Not yet, he's very high-spirited and always picking fights.

1

过了十天后，
Ten days later...

还不能，那只鸡只要看见别的鸡的影子，便会冲动起来。
Not yet, he'll attack whenever he sees even the shadow of another cock.

2

再过了十天，
Ten more days passed, and...

还不能。那只鸡常对四周怒目而视，它的气势自命不凡。
Still not ready yet, he's lunging like mad and willing to pick a fight with the air.

3

差不多可以了。它听见别的鸡叫已经没有反应，就像一只木鸡，它的心已不受外物所动。
Ok, I think he's finally ready. When he hears another cock crow, there's no reaction at all, he just stands there like he's made of wood.

又过了十天，
Ten days after that...

4

那太好了！
Excellent!

周宣王便使用那只鸡去斗鸡，别的鸡看它一动也不动，吓得连向它挑战也不敢了。
The king chose this cock for his next fight, and when the other cocks saw him just stand there without flinching, they fled in terror.

5

无心争斗的鸡，便全身无懈可击。它的劲气内敛，一触即发。
If we are at peace with ourselves and the world around us, success will come unsought.

附录 · 延伸阅读
APPENDIX Further reading

> 此部分为本书图画页的延伸阅读，
> 各段首所示的页码与图画页对应。

老子生平

P2　老子者，楚苦县厉乡曲仁里人也，姓李氏，名耳，字聃，周守藏室之史也。老子修道德，其学以自隐无名为务。居周久之，见周之衰，乃遂去。至关，关令尹喜曰："子将隐矣，强为我著书。"于是老子乃著书上下篇，言道德之意五千余言而去，莫知其所终。

P3~6　老子是楚国人，楚国位居中国的南方，这一点对他的思想有非常大的影响。因为南方风气柔弱，不像北方风气刚强，因此形成老子重视柔弱的思想。在《礼记》、《中庸》里，孔子就曾说过："宽柔以教，不报无道，南方之强也。衽金革，死而不厌，北方之强也。"……

我们看老子一再讲"守柔曰强"（五十二章）"柔弱胜刚强"（三十六章）"强梁者不得其死"（七十六章）这不是"宽柔以教"吗？老子又说："报怨以德"（七十九章）这不是"不报无道"吗？

老子所处的时代是春秋的晚期。这时候齐桓、晋文的霸业早已过去，而由南方蛮夷国吴越争霸。

老子虽和孔子处在同一时代，但是由于出身不同，地域各异，所以应付的方法也就不同。政治方面，他主张"无为"，赞成治政者"无常心，以百姓心为心"（四十九章）的民主。军事方面，他反对战争，他认为"兵者，不祥之器，物或恶之，故有道者不处。"（三十一章）社会伦理方面，他反对礼制，说"礼者，忠信之薄，而乱之首"。（三十八章）

P7　孔子适周，将问礼于老子。老子曰："子所言者，其人与骨皆已朽矣，独其言在耳。且君子得其时则驾，不得其时则蓬累而行。吾闻之，良贾深藏若虚，君子盛德，容貌若愚。去子之骄气与多欲，态色与淫志，是皆无益于子之身。吾所以告子，若是而已。"孔子去，谓弟子曰："鸟，吾知其能飞；鱼，吾知其能游；兽，吾知其能走。走者可以为罔，游者可以为纶，飞者可以为矰。至于龙，吾不能知其乘风云而上天。吾今日见老子，其犹龙邪！"

P13　现在一般通行的老子书，都分上下篇。上篇的第一句是"道可道，非常道"，下篇的第一句是"上德不德，是以有德"，因此后人就取上篇的"道"字和下篇的"德"字，合起来称它为《道德经》。

《史记·老子韩非列传》说："老子乃著书上下篇，言道德之意五千余言"，这和现行的《道德经》符合。

P14　"道"可道，非常"道"。

P15 名可名，非常"名"。"无"，名天地之始："有"，名万物之母。

P16 故常"无"，欲以观其妙；常"有"，欲以观其徼。

P17 此两者，同出而异名，同谓之玄。玄之又玄，众妙之门。

P18 天下皆知美之为美，斯恶已；皆知善之为善，斯不善已。
有无相生，难易相成，长短相形，高下相盈，音声相和，前后相随。

P19 是以圣人处无为之事，行不言之教。万物作而弗始，生而弗有，为而弗恃，功成而弗居。夫唯弗居，是以不去。

P20 不尚贤，使民不争；不贵难得之货，使民不为盗；不见可欲，使民心不乱。

P21 是以"圣人"之治，虚其心，实其腹，弱其志，强其骨。常使民无知无欲。使夫智者不敢为也。为"无为"，则无不治。

P22 "道"冲，而用之或不盈。渊兮，似万物之宗；湛兮，似或存。吾不知谁之子，象帝之先。

P23 天地不仁，以万物为刍狗；圣人不仁，以百姓为刍狗。

P24 天地之间，其犹橐籥乎？虚而不屈，动而愈出。
多言数穷，不如守中。

P25 天地长久。天地所以能长且久者，以其不自生，故能长生。
是以"圣人"后其身而身先；外其身而身存。非以其无私邪？故能成其私。

P26 上善若水。水善利万物而不争，处众人之所恶，故几于道。

P27 居善地，心善渊，与善仁，言善信，政善治，事善能，动善时。
夫唯不争，故无尤。

P28 持而盈之，不知其已；揣而锐之，不可长保。

P29 金玉满堂，莫之能守；富贵而骄，自遗其咎。功遂身退，天之道也。

P30 载营魄抱一，能无离乎？专气致柔，能如婴儿乎？涤除玄鉴，能无疵乎？爱国治民，能无为乎？天门开阖，能为雌乎？明白四达，能无知乎？

P31 三十辐，共一毂，当其无，有车之用。

埏埴以为器，当其无，有器之用。

P32　凿户牖以为室，当其无，有室之用。
故有之以为利，无之以为用。

P33　五色令人目盲；五音令人耳聋；五味令人口爽。

P34　驰骋畋猎，令人心发狂；难得之货，令人行妨。
是以圣人为腹不为目，故去彼取此。

P35　宠辱若惊，贵大患若身。
何谓宠辱若惊？宠为下，得之若惊，失之若惊，是谓宠辱若惊。

P36　何谓贵大患若身？吾所以有大患者，为吾有身，及吾无身，吾有何患？
故贵以身为天下，若可寄天下。爱以身为天下，若可托天下。

P37　致虚极，守静笃。
万物并作，吾以观复。
夫物芸芸，各复归其根。

P38　归根曰静，静曰复命。复命曰常，知常曰明。不知常，妄作凶。
知常容，容乃公，公乃全，全乃天，天乃道，道乃久。没身不殆。

P39　太上，不知有之；其次，亲而誉之；其次，畏之；其次，侮之。

P40　信不足焉，有不信焉。
悠兮其贵言。功成事遂，百姓皆谓："我自然。"

P41　大道废，有仁义；智慧出，有大伪；

P42　六亲不和，有孝慈；国家昏乱，有忠臣。

P43　唯之与阿，相去几何？善之与恶，相去若何？人之所畏，不可不畏。
荒兮，其未央哉！

P44　众人熙熙，如享太牢，如春登台。我独泊兮，其未兆，沌沌兮如婴儿之未孩。儽儽兮，若无所归。
众人皆有余，而我独若遗。我愚人之心也哉！俗人昭昭，我独昏昏。俗人察察，我独闷闷。
众人皆有以，而我独顽且鄙。我独异于人，而贵食母。

P45 曲则全，枉则直，洼则盈，敝则新，少则得，多则惑。

P46 是以"圣人"抱一为天下式。不自见，故明；不自是，故彰；不自伐，故有功；不自矜，故长。

夫唯不争，故天下莫能与之争。古之所谓"曲则全"者，岂虚言哉！诚全而归之。

P47 夫兵者，不祥之器，物或恶之，故有道者不处。

君子居则贵左，用兵则贵右。

P48 兵者不祥之器，非君子之器，不得已而用之，恬淡为上。胜而不美，而美之者，是乐杀人。夫乐杀人者，则不可得志于天下矣。

吉事尚左，凶事尚右。偏将军居左，上将军居右，言以丧礼处之。杀人之众，以悲哀泣之，战胜以丧礼处之。

P49 知人者智，自知者明。胜人者力，自胜者强。知足者富，强行者有志。

P50 不失其所者久。死而不亡者寿。

P51 执大象，天下往。往而不害，安平太。

乐与饵，过客止。"道"之出口，淡乎其无味，视之不足见，听之不足闻，用之不足既。

P52 将欲歙之，必固张之；将欲弱之，必固强之；将欲废之，必固兴之；将欲取之，必固与之。是谓微明。

柔弱胜刚强。鱼不可脱于渊，国之利器，不可以示人。

P54 谷神不死，是谓玄牝。

玄牝之门，是谓天地根。

绵绵若存，用之不勤。

P55 视之不见，名曰夷，听之不闻，名曰希，搏之不得，名曰微。此三者不可致诘，故混而为一。其上不皦，其下不昧，绳绳兮不可名，复归于无物。是谓无状之状，无物之象，是谓惚恍。

P56 迎之不见其首，随之不见其后。

执古之道，以御今之有。

能知古始，是谓道纪。

P57 古之善为道者，微妙玄通，深不可识。夫唯不可识，故强为之容；豫兮若冬涉川；犹兮若畏四邻，俨兮其若客。

P58 涣兮若冰之将释；敦兮其若朴；旷兮其若谷；混兮其若浊。

P59 孰能浊以静之徐清；孰能安以久动之徐生。保此道者，不欲盈。夫唯不盈，故能蔽而新成。

P60 绝圣弃智，民利百倍；
绝仁弃义，民复孝慈；
绝巧弃利，盗贼无有。
此三者以为文不足，故令有所属：见素抱朴，少私寡欲，绝学无忧。

P61 孔"德"之容，唯"道"是从。"道"之为物，惟恍惟惚。惚兮恍兮，其中有象；恍兮惚兮，其中有物。

P62 窈兮冥兮，其中有精。其精甚真，其中有信。
自今及古，其名不去，以阅众甫。吾何以知众甫之状哉？以此。

P63 希言自然。
故飘风不终朝，骤雨不终日。孰为此者？天地。

P64 天地尚不能久，而况于人乎？故从事于"道"者，同于"道"；"德"者，同于"德"；失者，同于失。同于"道"者，"道"亦乐得之；

P65 同于"德"者，"德"亦乐得之；同于失者，失亦乐得之。信不足焉，有不信焉。

P66 企者不立；跨者不行。自见者不明；自是者不彰；自伐者无功；自矜者不长。

P67 其在道也，曰：余食赘形。物或恶之，故有道者不处。

P68 有物混成，先天地生。寂兮寥兮，独立而不改，周行而不殆，可以为天地母。吾不知其名，强字之曰"道"。

P69 强为之名曰"大"。大曰逝，逝曰远，远曰反。
故"道"大，天大，地大，人亦大。域中有四大，而人居其一焉。
人法地，地法天，天法"道"，"道"法自然。

P70 重为轻根，静为躁君。
是以君子终日行不离辎重，虽有荣观，燕处超然。

P71 奈何万乘之主，而以身轻天下？轻则失根，躁则失君。

P72 善行无辙迹；善言无瑕谪；善数不用筹策；善闭无关楗而不可开；

P73 善结无绳约而不可解。

是以圣人常善救人，故无弃人；常善救物，故无弃物。是谓袭明。

P74 故善人者，不善人之师；不善人者，善人之资。不贵其师，不爱其资，虽智大迷。是谓要妙。

P75 知其雄，守其雌，为天下谿。为天下谿，常德不离，复归于婴儿。

P76 知其白，（守其黑，为天下式。为天下式，常德不忒，复归于无极。知其荣，）守其辱，为天下谷。为天下谷，常德乃足，复归于朴。

P77 朴散则为器，圣人用之，则为官长，故大制不割。

P78 将欲取天下而为之，吾见其不得已。天下神器，不可为也，（不可执也。）为者败之，执者失之。

P79 夫物或行或随；或歔或吹；或强或羸；或载或隳。
是以圣人去甚，去奢，去泰。

P80 以道佐人主者，不以兵强天下。其事好还。师之所处，荆棘生焉。大军之后，必有凶年。
善者果而已，不敢以取强。

P81 果而勿矜，果而勿伐，果而勿骄。果而不得已，果而勿强。
物壮则老，是谓不道，不道早已。

P82 "道"常无名，朴。虽小，天下莫能臣。侯王若能守之，万物将自宾。
天地相合，以降甘露，民莫之令而自均。

P83 始制有名，名亦既有，夫亦将知止，知止可以不殆。
譬"道"之在天下，犹川谷之于江海。

P84 大道泛兮，其可左右。万物恃之以生而不辞，功成而不有。衣养万物而不为主，可名于小；万物归焉而不为主，可名为大。以其终不自为大，故能成其大。

P85 "道"常无为而无不为。侯王若能守之，万物将自化。化而欲作，吾将镇之以无名之朴。镇之以无名之朴，夫将不欲。不欲以静，天下将自正。

P87 上"德"不"德"，是以有"德"；下"德"不失"德"，是以无"德"。
上"德"无为而无以为；下"德"无为而有以为。
上"仁"为之而无以为；上"义"为之而有以为。

P88 上"礼"为之而莫之应，则攘臂而扔之。故失"道"而后"德"，失"德"而后"仁"，失

184

"仁"而后"义"，失"义"而后"礼"。

夫"礼"者，忠信之薄，而乱之首。前识者，"道"之华，而愚之始。是以大丈夫处其厚，不居其薄；处其实，不居其华。故去彼取此。

P89 反者"道"之动；弱者"道"之用。

天下万物生于"有"，而"有"生于"无"。

P90 "道"生一，一生二，二生三，三生万物。万物负阴而抱阳，冲气以为和。

P91 天下之至柔，驰骋天下之至坚。无有入无间，吾是以知无为之有益。不言之教，无为之益，天下希及之。

P92 名与身孰亲？身与货孰多？得与亡孰病？

甚爱必大费；多藏必厚亡。

知足不辱，知止不殆，可以长久。

P93 天下有道，却走马以粪。天下无道，戎马生于郊。

P94 福莫大于不知足；咎莫大于欲得。故知足之足，常足矣。

P95 不出户，知天下；不窥牖，见天"道"。其出弥远，其知弥少。

是以"圣人"不行而知，不见而明，不为而成。

P96 为学日益，为"道"日损。损之又损，以至于无为。无为而无不为。取天下常以无事，及其有事，不足以取天下。

P97 "圣人"无常心，以百姓心为心。

善者，吾善之，不善者，吾亦善之；德善。

信者，吾信之，不信者，吾亦信之；德信。

"圣人"在天下，歙歙焉，为天下浑其心，百姓皆注其耳目，"圣人"皆孩之。

P98 出生入死。生之徒，十有三；死之徒，十有三，人之生，动之于死地，亦十有三。

夫何故？以其生生之厚。

P99 盖闻善摄生者，陆行不遇兕虎，入军不被甲兵；兕无所投其角，虎无所用其爪，兵无所容其刃。

P100 夫何故？以其无死地。

P101 知者不言，言者不知。

挫其锐，解其纷，和其光，同其尘，是谓"玄同"。故不可得而亲，不可得而疏；不可得而利，不可得而害；不可得而贵，不可得而贱。故为天下贵。

P102 以正治国，以奇用兵，以无事取天下。吾何以知其然哉?

P103 以此：天下多忌讳，而民弥贫；人多利器，国家滋昏；人多伎巧，奇物滋起，法令滋彰，盗贼多有。

P104 治大国，若烹小鲜。
以"道"莅天下，其鬼不神；非其鬼不神，其神不伤人；非其神不伤人，"圣人"亦不伤人。夫两不相伤，故"德"交归焉。

P105 江海之所以能为百谷王者，以其善下之，故能为百谷王。
是以"圣人"欲上民，必以言下之；欲先民，必以身后之。是以"圣人"处上而民不重，处前而民不害。是以天下乐推而不厌。以其不争，故天下莫能与之争。

P106 善为士者不武，善战者，不怒，善胜敌者，不与，善用人者，为之下。 是谓不争之德，是谓用人之力，是谓配天古之极。

P107 知不知，尚矣；不知知，病也。 圣人不病，以其病病。夫唯病病，是以不病。

P108 勇于敢则杀，勇于不敢则活。 此两者，或利或害。

P109 天之所恶，孰知其故? 天之道，不争而善胜，不言而善应，不召而自来，繟然而善谋。天网恢恢，疏而不失。

P110 人之生也柔弱，其死也坚强。
草木之生也柔脆，其死也枯槁。
故坚强者死之徒，柔弱者生之徒。

P111 是以兵强则灭，木强则折。
强大处下，柔弱处上。

P112 天下莫柔弱于水，而攻坚强者莫之能胜，以其无以易之。
弱之胜强，柔之胜刚，天下莫不知，莫能行。
是以"圣人"云："受国之垢，是谓社稷主：受国不祥，是为天下王。"正言若反。

P113 和大怨，必有余怨；安可以为善?
是以"圣人"执左契，而不责于人。有"德"司契，无"德"司彻。
天道无亲，常与善人。

P114　信言不美，美言不信。

善者不辩，辩者不善。

知者不博，博者不知。

P115　"圣人"不积，既以为人己愈有，既以与人己愈多。

天之道，利而不害；"圣人"之道，为而不争。

P117　昔之得"一"者，天得"一"以清，地得"一"以宁，神得"一"以灵，谷得"一"以盈，

P118　万物得"一"以生，侯王得"一"以为天下正。其致之也，谓天无以清，将恐裂，地无以宁，将恐废，神无以灵，将恐歇，

P119　谷无以盈，将恐竭；万物无以生，将恐灭；侯王无以正，将恐蹶。故贵以贱为本，高以下为基。

P120　是以侯王自称孤、寡、不榖，此非以贱为本邪？非乎？故至誉无誉。是故不欲琭琭如玉，珞珞如石。

P121　上士闻道，勤而行之；中士闻道，若存若亡；下士闻道，大笑之，不笑不足以为道。

P122　故建言有之：明道若昧，进道若退，夷道若类。上德若谷，广德若不足。

P123　建德若偷，质真若渝。大白若辱，大方无隅，大器晚成；

P124　大音希声，大象无形，"道"隐无名。夫唯"道"，善贷且成。

P125　大成若缺，其用不弊。

大盈若冲，其用不穷。

P126　大直若屈，大巧若拙，大辩若讷。

静胜躁，寒胜热。清静为天下正。

P127　"道"生之，"德"畜之，物形之，势成之。

是以万物莫不尊"道"而贵"德"。

"道"之尊，"德"之贵，夫莫之命而常自然。

P128　故"道"生之，"德"畜之；长之育之；亭之毒之；养之覆之。

生而不有；为而不恃，长而不宰。是谓"玄德"。

P129　天下有始，以为天下母。既得其母，以知其子；既知其子，复守其母，没身不殆。塞其兑，

闭其门，终身不勤。

P130 开其兑，济其事，终身不救。
见小曰"明"，守柔曰"强"。用其光，复归其明，无遗身殃；是为袭"常"。

P131 使我介然有知，行于大道，唯施是畏。
大道甚夷，而人好径。朝甚除，田甚芜，仓甚虚；

P132 服文彩，带利剑，厌饮食，财货有余；是谓盗夸。非道也哉！

P133 善建者不拔，善抱者不脱，子孙以祭祀不辍。
修之于身，其德乃真；修之于家，其德乃余；修之于乡，其德乃长；修之于邦，其德乃丰；修之于天下，其德乃普。

P134 故以身观身，以家观家，以乡观乡，以邦观邦，以天下观天下。吾何以知天下然哉？以此。

P135 含"德"之厚，比于赤子。毒虫不螫，猛兽不据，攫鸟不搏。骨弱筋柔而握固。

P136 未知牝牡之合而全作，精之至也。终日号而不嗄，和之至也。
知和曰"常"，知常曰"明"。益生曰祥。

P137 心使气曰强。物壮则老，谓之不道，不道早已。

P138 其政闷闷，其民淳淳；其政察察，其民缺缺。
祸兮，福之所倚；福兮，祸之所伏。孰知其极？

P139 其无正也。正复为奇，善复为妖。人之迷，其日固久。
是以圣人方而不割，廉而不刿，直而不肆，光而不耀。

P140 治人事天，莫若啬。
夫唯啬，是谓早服；早服谓之重积德；重积德则无不克；

P141 无不克则莫知其极；莫知其极，可以有国；有国之母，可以长久；是谓深根固柢，长生久视之道。

P142 大邦者下流，天下之牝。天下之交也。牝常以静胜牡，以静为下。
故大邦以下小邦，则取小邦；小邦以下大邦，则取大邦。

P143 故或下以取，或下而取。大邦不过欲兼畜人，小邦不过欲入事人。夫两者各得所欲，大者宜为下。

P144 "道"者万物之奥。善人之宝，不善人之所保。
美言可以市尊，美行可以加人。人之不善，何弃之有？

P145 故立天子，置三公，虽有拱璧以先驷马，不如坐进此道。
古之所以贵此道者何？不曰：求以得，有罪以免邪？故为天下贵。

P146 为无为，事无事，味无味。
图难于其易，为大于其细；天下难事，必作于易，天下大事，必作于细。

P147 是以圣人终不为大，故能成其大。
夫轻诺必寡信；多易必多难。是以圣人犹难之，故终无难矣。

P148 其安易持，其未兆易谋。其脆易泮，其微易散。
为之于未有，治之于未乱。

P149 合抱之木，生于毫末；九层之台，起于累土；千里之行，始于足下。
民之从事，常于几成而败之。慎终如始，则无败事。

P150 古之善为道者，非以明民，将以愚之。
民之难治，以其智多。故以智治国，国之贼；不以智治国，国之福。

P151 知此两者亦稽式。常知稽式，是谓"玄德"，"玄德"深矣，远矣，与物反矣，然后乃至大顺。

P152 我有三宝，持而保之。一曰慈，二曰俭，三曰不敢为天下先。
慈故能勇；俭故能广；不敢为天下先，故能成器长。

P153 今舍慈且勇；舍俭且广；舍后且先；死矣！
夫慈，以战则胜，以守则固。天将救之，以慈卫之。

P154 用兵有言："吾不敢为主，而为客；不敢进寸，而退尺。"是谓行无行；攘无臂；扔无敌；执无兵。

P155 祸莫大于轻敌，轻敌几丧吾宝。故抗兵相若，哀者胜矣。

P156 吾言甚易知，甚易行。
天下莫能知，莫能行。
言有宗，事有君。夫唯无知，是以不我知。

P157 知我者希，则我者贵。

是以圣人被褐而怀玉。

P158 民不畏威，则大威至。
无狎其所居，无厌其所生。
夫唯不厌，是以不厌。

P159 是以圣人自知不自见；自爱不自贵。
故去彼取此。

P160 民不畏死，奈何以死惧之？若使民常畏死，而为奇者，吾得执而杀之，孰敢？

P161 常有司杀者杀。夫代司杀者杀，是谓代大匠斫，夫代大匠斫者，希有不伤其手矣。

P162 民之饥，以其上食税之多，是以饥。
民之难治，以其上之有为，是以难治。
民之轻死，以其上求生之厚，是以轻死。
夫唯无以生为者，是贤于贵生。

P163 天之道，其犹张弓与？高者抑之，下者举之；有余者损之，不足者补之。

P164 天之道，损有余而补不足。
人之道，则不然，损不足以奉有余。
孰能有余以奉天下？唯有道者。

P165 小国寡民。使有什伯之器而不用；使民重死而不远徙。虽有舟舆，无所乘之；虽有甲兵，无所陈之。

P166 使民复结绳而用之。甘其食，美其服，安其居，乐其俗。

P167 邻国相望，鸡犬之声相闻，民至老死，不相往来。

P169 道可道，非常道。

———《道德经》第一章

P171 名可名，非常名。

———《道德经》第一章

P172 太上，不知有之。

———《道德经》第十七章

P173　人法地，地法天，天法道，道法自然。

——《道德经》第二十五章

P174　上德不德，是以有德；下德不失德，是以无德。

——《道德经》第三十八章

P175　祸莫大于不知足，咎莫大于欲得。

——《道德经》第四十六章

P176　知者不言，言者不知。

——《道德经》第五十六章

P177　天下多忌讳，而民弥贫；
朝多利器，国家滋昏；
人多伎巧，奇物滋起。

——《道德经》第五十七章

P178　善为士者，不武；
善战者，不怒；
善战敌者，不与。

——《道德经》第六十八章